1976

Don't Drink the Water

Don't Drink the Water

WOODY ALLEN

ew York

L.C. #67-22663

Photographs by courtesy of Friedman-Abeles

MANUFACTURED IN THE UNITED STATES OF AMERICA

DON'T DRINK THE WATER *was first presented on November 17, 1966, by David Merrick in association with Jack Rollins and Charles Joffe at the Morosco Theatre in New York City, with the following cast:*

(In Order of Appearance)

FATHER DROBNEY	Dick Libertini
AMBASSADOR JAMES F. MAGEE	House Jameson
KILROY	Gerry Matthews
AXEL MAGEE	Anthony Roberts
MARION HOLLANDER	Kay Medford
WALTER HOLLANDER	Lou Jacobi
SUSAN HOLLANDER	Anita Gillette
KROJACK	James Dukas
BURNS	Curtis Wheeler
CHEF	Gene Varrone
THE SULTAN OF BASHIR	Oliver Clark
SULTAN'S 1ST WIFE	Donna Mills
KASNAR	John Hallow
COUNTESS BORDONI	Sharon Talbot
NOVOTNY	Luke Andreas

Directed by Stanley Prager
Associate Producer Samuel Liff
Setting and Lighting by Jo Mielziner
Costumes by Motley

SYNOPSIS OF SCENES

The action of the play takes place in an American Embassy somewhere behind the Iron Curtain.

ACT ONE

ACT TWO

Act One

The house lights dim and we hear what sounds like the national anthem of some Middle-European country, very martial and pompous and official. After a chorus of it the music sounds as though it were being played at too fast a speed. The house lights go out and the curtain rises on the American Embassy in a small Iron Curtain country somewhere in Eastern Europe. It is a very small but very quaint, charming, "old world" mansion, done in the ultimate of elegance. The walls are beautifully wood-panelled and mirrored. The chandeliers are lovely.

Upstage center there are two large doors that open to the front portion of the building or the portion that faces out onto the street. This front porch, as we can occasionally see when the doors are left open, is a lovely black and white tiled hall which serves as the center reception area when someone enters the building. (Presumably one enters, is greeted in this receiving area by a gentleman who sits at a desk situated there, and is given directions to any of several rooms, depending on his business.)

There is one main room, where much of the play's action occurs. There are other rooms, such as a tiny auditorium on the second floor, with a large, dominating portrait of the President of the United States, and also several minor rooms on the first floor that are used for filing, a small business office for the Ambassador and one for his assistant, and probably a small, tastefully furnished smoking room or conference room—but this main room is the nucleus of the place. Here the dignitaries discuss, chat, have drinks; plans are laid, negotiations felt out; small parties or receptions are usually held

3

*in this room also, although guests spill out into other parts
of the building.*

*The main room is furnished with that sparse elegance that
one might find in one of the rooms in the White House like
the Blue Room or the Red Room. Small areas for conversation here and there, perhaps for tea or brandy, a prim sofa,
a small leathertop desk with phone that is quite antique,
magnificent, waxed wood floors, and maybe one lovely area
rug to contribute to this simple but rich-looking room. There
are open doors stage left and stage right for this room, because of its central location.*

The time is the present.

The stage is empty.

*From down the upstage staircase comes the specter-like,
tall, emaciated, cassocked figure of* FATHER DROBNEY, *a priest
who speaks with an accent. He faces the audience and one
can detect behind his eyes the faint glimmer of an eccentric.*

DROBNEY   Good evening. My name is Drobney. Father Drobney. I am a priest in this charming little Communist country where out of four million inhabitants, 3,975,000 are
atheists, and about 24,000 are agnostics—and the other thousand are Jewish. The point is: I don't have a big following.
This is the United States Embassy of this country. Six years
ago I ran in here seeking asylum from the Communist
police. Outside these walls were four million Communists
determined to kill me! My choice was simple. I could remain here in the safety of your embassy, or I could go outside and attempt the biggest mass conversion in history. I
decided to stay and I've been hiding upstairs ever since.
The head of this Embassy is Ambassador James F. Magee.
He was put in charge here by your government because
of his firm grasp of world events. (*Enter* AMBASSADOR

4

MAGEE, *hard-nosed, dignified, in his mid-fifties, a career-organization-team man. He goes right to a window and looks out*) Each morning for the past four years he enters this room, surveys the environment, and graces us with his clarity and wisdom.

AMBASSADOR   Jesus, look at all those Communists!

DROBNEY   This is typical of his ability to sum up a situation brilliantly. (AMBASSADOR MAGEE *goes to the desk and loads his briefcase with papers for a trip.* KILROY *enters with a pad and pencil, poised at the* AMBASSADOR's *side.* KILROY *is a punctilious rat—you can smell his type a mile away*) Mr. Kilroy is Ambassador Magee's bright-eyed, efficient assistant.

KILROY (*Stage front*)   I am the only man in the Foreign Service who knows the words to the second stanza of the Star-Spangled Banner.

DROBNEY   All of his vital memos are sent through Mr. Kilroy.

AMBASSADOR   Mr. Kilroy, take a vital memo: To all Embassy personnel: Until a new embassy building is purchased, we must think of new ways to make room in this small mansion. It was unfortunate that when Dean Rusk passed through the country last week we were unable to put him up for the night. It was equally unfortunate that no one here recognized him. See this does not happen again.

(KILROY *exits smartly. Enter* AXEL MAGEE, *about*

*twenty-eight, a pleasant well-meaning young man
whose career in the Foreign Service has been a series
of disasters. He is always trying but somehow everything always manages to go wrong for him)*

DROBNEY   And this is Ambassador Magee's other assistant.
Not exactly bright-eyed, not exactly efficient, in fact the
only man in the history of the Foreign Service to accidentally wrap his lunch in a peace treaty.

MAGEE   (*Stage front*)   I've worked in seventeen U. S. Em-
bassies. Some for as long as three weeks.

DROBNEY   This young man has worked at this Embassy
for six months. That's the longest he's ever worked at any
one Embassy. Why? Because he's pleasant, he's eager, and
he's the Ambassador's son.

MAGEE   You sent for me, Dad?

DROBNEY   And here is where it all starts. I better get back
to my room.
      (*He exits upstairs*)

AMBASSADOR   Axel, because of my superior record here, the
leaders of my party would like to discuss the possibility of
placing my name in the coming gubernatorial race in our
state.

MAGEE   Dad, I think you'd make a wonderful governor. Your
broad outlook would appeal to psychotic liberals as well as
militant fascists. Something for everyone.

AMBASSADOR   Naturally, in my absence this Embassy must

be run with the same brilliant efficiency it is accustomed to when I am here.

MAGEE   This is a quiet little outpost. There should be no trouble.

AMBASSADOR   I'll level with you, Axel. I'm tempted to leave Mr. Kilroy in charge, but it looks bad for the family image.

MAGEE   Dad, the Foreign Service is my whole life. Give me a chance to prove myself once and for all. What can go wrong in two weeks?

AMBASSADOR   You were in Brazil for two weeks and you had them importing coffee!

MAGEE   Dad, I know how much that governorship means to you and I'll see that this Embassy remains a credit to your record.

AMBASSADOR   The only important guest we're going to have in the next two weeks is the Sultan of Bashir.

MAGEE   I'll see that the Sultan gets royal treatment.

AMBASSADOR   You sure will, Axel. I'm on the verge of concluding an oil deal with the Sultan that will make me a very big man next November. Axel, most fathers start their sons in the mail room and let them work their way up. I started you on top and you worked your way to the mail room. This Embassy is a clean start for you. If it's not run letter perfect, I'll fire you, and if your own father fires

7

you—it's the end of the line. Good-bye.
(*He exits*)

MAGEE Have a good flight, Dad. (*He looks around, and straightens up confidently*) Mr. Kilroy!

KILROY You called?

MAGEE For the next two weeks I am in charge of this Embassy. Business will go on as usual, and it would mean a great deal to me to have your full cooperation.

KILROY Your father should have known better than to leave in charge a man who was asked to leave Africa.

MAGEE That's not fair. Some of the best men in the Foreign Service have at one time or another been recalled from a country.

KILROY Africa is a continent. You've been recalled from an entire continent. And what about Japan, you never mention that, or the Soviet Union—you managed to cover that up, too.

MAGEE You know I've had some bad breaks careerwise.

KILROY (*Accusingly*) And you were hung in effigy in Panama!

MAGEE I admitted I was!

KILROY Yes, but you didn't say it was by our own Embassy! (*The phone rings. They both go for it. KILROY then realizes who's in charge and lets MAGEE pick it up*)

MAGEE (*Into the phone*) Yes? Yes, this is the American Embassy . . . oh, no, Ambassador Magee is not here. He's on his way back to the United States. This is Axel Magee. I'm in charge during his absence. (*Gunshots just outside the Embassy are heard*) What the hell is that all about?
(*He slams down the phone*)

KILROY (*He goes to the window*) It's the Communist police! They're chasing three people—they look like tourists. Mr. Magee, they're running up the steps of the Embassy!

MAGEE We better open the front door quickly!
(*He runs and opens the doors. In burst* MR. *and* MRS. WALTER HOLLANDER *and their daughter* SUSAN. MR. HOLLANDER *is a typical tourist complete with loud, short-sleeved shirt worn outside his pants, and a green hat. He is carrying a camera. His wife carries a TWA bag. The* HOLLANDERS *are a family from Newark, on vacation. They are in their early fifties and, despite their comical appearance, have a beautiful daughter of about twenty-three. But we will come to that. Right now they are in a stage of hysteria and fear*)

MARION HOLLANDER Help! We're American tourists! The Communists are after us! They think we're spies!
(*Gunshots ring out*)

WALTER We're Americans! I swear! Willie Mays! Hershey Bars! Kate Smith! I pledge allegiance to the flag!

MARION And to the republic for which it stands!
(*More gunshots are heard*)

SUSAN   It's the Communist police.

WALTER   Some vacation . . . Run!
(*The* HOLLANDERS *run off,* SUSAN *separating from her parents and heading up and off.* WALTER *and* MARION *hide in an adjacent office. An armed Communist* GUARD *enters looking for them, followed by* KROJACK, *menacing and vicious head of the secret police. He wears a business suit and carries an automatic*)

KROJACK   Where are they? Hand them over to us.

MAGEE   Who? What? What did they do?

KROJACK   (*In a booming voice*)   They were caught in the act of spying!

MAGEE   How?

KROJACK   They were taking pictures in a restricted area.
(*The* GUARD *holds fast and waits orders*)

MAGEE   That doesn't make them spies. They're American tourists—didn't you see the shirt that guy was wearing? What did they take pictures of?

KROJACK   Missile sites and rocket installations . . . They have seen too much, they must die.

BURNS   (*Bursting in, frightened*)   Mr. Magee, they're setting up searchlights and machine guns around the Embassy.

MAGEE   (*To* KROJACK)   I'm sure they didn't realize . . . Look, I'll give you the film. In fact, I'll give you the whole camera.

KROJACK (*Viciously*) Hand them over to us or we will drag them out and shoot them!

MAGEE (*Taking a stand*) This Embassy is United States territory. Nobody can be dragged out of here and shot without the written consent of the American government.

KILROY (*To* KROJACK) Leave these premises at once. Your behavior is in extreme violation of international conduct.

KROJACK (*Looks at* KILROY, *then at* MAGEE) Who are you?

MAGEE I'm Axel Magee. I am in charge of this Embassy in my father's absence and I order you to leave at once. Guns or no guns—if you don't go, Mr. Kilroy will throw you out.
(*The* CHEF, *a temperamental eccentric, enters in a tizzy*)

CHEF Mr. Magee—something is happening!

MAGEE Yes, Hatami, I know . . .

CHEF There are soldiers surrounding the house. They are staring into the kitchen!

MAGEE They won't hurt you.

CHEF (*Suddenly an "artist"*) I can't cook if I'm being stared at. I'm that kind of person.

KROJACK Who are you?

CHEF I am personal chef to Ambassador Magee, formerly chef to the King of Norway—formerly chef at the White

House—formerly chef to the Queen of England . . . Before
that I did very little cooking.

MAGEE   Don't you terrorize our help!

CHEF   (*With bravado*)   I had a cake in the oven! Your
gunshots made it fall!
   (*He exits in high dudgeon*)

KILROY   Mr. Magee, stand firm—I'll lodge a formal protest.
   (*He exits*)

MAGEE   *You* stand firm, *I'll* . . . lodge . . . (*Now* MAGEE
is alone facing the guns) Look—you spy on us—we spy on
you—everybody knows it. Why do we suddenly pretend
it's so unusual?

KROJACK   (*Seizes on this*)   You do spy on us?

MAGEE   Huh?

KROJACK   (*It interests him*)   How often?

MAGEE   (*Trying to calm things down*)   All the time. It's no
secret. Espionage goes on between our countries every day.
Why be so hypocritical about it?

KROJACK   It does, huh. And are *they* spies?

MAGEE   No . . . maybe . . . I don't know . . .

KROJACK   How do you know they're not spies? You never
saw them before?

MAGEE   Are you going to tell me your country doesn't send spies into the United States posing as tourists?

KROJACK (*Pressing him*)   Then you admit they're spies?

MAGEE (*Just trying to be civilized*)   What if they are? That doesn't give you the right to enter this building illegally. You're going to start an international incident. This is not just an outrage but a vicious and cruel attack on the whole free world. I wouldn't be surprised if France took our side.
        (KILROY *enters*)

KILROY   Mr. Krojack—I have your foreign affairs office on the phone. They want you to report back immediately.

KROJACK   He admitted they are spies.

KILROY (*Stunned*)   You didn't, Mr. Magee!

MAGEE   Ah, well, er . . . ah . . .

KROJACK   He admitted it. I have it all here on tape.
        (*He produces a miniature tape recorder from his pocket*)

MAGEE   I did—in a sense—Mr. Kilroy. You know, we spy— they spy . . .

KILROY (*Yelling into the tape recorder*)   We do nothing of the sort!

MAGEE (*Trying to smooth things over but making them worse*) Actually we do, if we all stop being hypocritical and be honest for once . . .

KILROY (*Turning on him*)   That's enough, Mr. Magee!

MAGEE   We do spy!

KROJACK (*He extends the tape recorder*)   Will you speak louder, please.

MAGEE   Now, look, don't twist my words. You come barging in here with guns—then wonder why a brutal dictatorship gets a bad name!

KROJACK   The Embassy will be surrounded from this day on. The spies will either come out, or spend the rest of their lives in here. But first the *world* will hear this confession. Good-bye for now.
      (*He motions the* GUARD *to come. They exit*)

KILROY   How could you do it? How could you admit they were spies?

MAGEE   I panicked. I lost control.

KILROY   What were you thinking?

MAGEE   I was thinking *don't panic! Don't lose control!*
      (WALTER *and* MARION *enter from the next room*)

WALTER   You!

MAGEE   Who?

WALTER   Yeh! You with the vest. Why did you tell them we're spies?

MARION Walter—be careful. (*To no one in particular*) He's always eavesdropping.

WALTER How could you tell them we're spies? They say we're spies, he tells 'em yes. All of a sudden I'm a spy. I'll go on "What's My Line?"—they'll never guess.

MARION Where's my daughter?

KILROY I'll get her. Mr. Burns. Bring the girl up from the basement.

MAGEE Yes, Mr. Burns, bring the girl up from the basement.

WALTER What are you—his echo?

MARION Walter, be quiet.

WALTER Those lunatics out there accuse us of spying, and this lunatic says yes.

MAGEE If you were listening to the conversation you should know that I was trying to calm them down.

MARION First no movie on the plane—then this.

MAGEE It's a simple misunderstanding.

MARION How simple?

WALTER (*To* MARION) If we leave the building they kill us. Simple enough?

MAGEE   Don't jump to conclusions. There'd be a trial first.
(*He stepped in it again*)

WALTER   Who is this guy?

KILROY   (*To* MAGEE)   I'd better call your father. Maybe I
can stop him at the airport.
(*He starts toward the next office*)

MAGEE   There's no need for that. I can handle a crisis.

KILROY   Handle one. You are one.
(*He exits*)

WALTER   A man takes his family on vacation—he wants to
show them a good time—this is what we have working in
our government. Then they wonder why I don't vote.

MAGEE   I've got to make out a report.
(*He clumsily begins picking up all the loose forms
from the desk*)

MARION   Well, that's what you get for taking pictures.

WALTER   It's my vacation. My new hobby is photography.
Am I interested in their missiles and rockets? All I want
to do is take some pictures.

MAGEE   I wonder if your photos are valuable?

MARION   He held the camera backwards. They're pictures of
his nose.

WALTER   I gotta have my head examined. Every time I listen to you I wind up behind the eightball.

MARION   Here we go again.

WALTER   If you had listened to me, we would've taken a cabana in Atlantic Beach.

MARION   Every year it must be Atlantic Beach. What's the matter, they need you to work the tide?

WALTER   No, we had to go to Europe. Thirty-five hundred dollars for three weeks of uninterrupted diarrhea.

MARION   What's so terrible? My brother suggested we see Europe. He had a wonderful time here.

WALTER   I'm tired of living for your brother. (*To* MAGEE) I have to run my life by her brother. That's a hot one.

MAGEE   I realize you're upset—if I could just get some facts . . .

MARION   Mr. and Mrs. Walter Hollander, Newark, New Jersey.

WALTER   You want to know the facts? The facts are I have a three-week vacation. I said, let's take a cabana at Atlantic Beach—there's sun, you can play pinochle, there's miniature golf. No, her brother says, go to Europe. And behind the Iron Curtain no less. I needed this like a growth.

MARION   Aren't you interested in how the other half lives? We went with you to the Folies Bergère in Paris.

WALTER   Are you comparing Communism to those girls?

MARION (*To* MAGEE)   As if he appreciates Europe anyplace. We took him to Westminster Abbey, his feet hurt. We took him to St. Peter's in Rome, he got dizzy from looking up. We took him to the Louve—I hate to tell you what happened.

WALTER   It's pronounced Louv-*re*—Louv-*re* . . . that's how much you know.

MARION   In the Louv-*re* he struck a match across a Van Gogh. I thought I'd die.

MAGEE (*Trying to fill out the forms*)   Have either of you two ever had any respiratory ailments— Oh, wrong forms.

MARION (*To* MAGEE)   I have a brother, see? He's a wonderful man.

WALTER   He's a Nazi.

MARION   Do you know what you're talking about?

WALTER (*To* MAGEE)   Take my word for it—he should be wearing an armband.

MAGEE (*Trying to find the correct form*)   Here we are . . . seeking asylum.

WALTER   I'm not seeking asylum. I didn't do anything. I'm a caterer from New Jersey.

MAGEE   I'll need your passports and I have to get some information.

MARION I'm giving you information. It began with my brother—quite a lovely individual.

WALTER They should have hung him at Nuremberg.

MAGEE (*Consulting the form*) Have you ever bought anything on credit?
(*He realizes it's wrong again, and runs to get another form*)

MARION My brother went to Europe last year. He had a wonderful time. He suggested we bring my daughter—it's cultural. My brother is an intellectual.

WALTER Some intellectual. Like Sonny Liston.

MAGEE And you're just a caterer. Nobody paid you to take pictures of anything, or anything like that . . .

WALTER Hollander and Blackwell—finest in Newark. Here's my card.

MAGEE Do you work, Mrs. Hollander?

MARION No, sir. I'm an average housewife.

WALTER Some housewife. She's a professional mah-jongg hustler. She carries around her own tiles.

MAGEE And you accidentally wandered into a restricted area. I mean, you didn't sneak in or anything . . .

MARION I told him it looked like private property, but he had to get a photograph. He said, "Why? 'Cause there's guards and dogs and barbed wire?" I said, "Yes, 'cause there's guards and dogs and barbed wire." (*Turning on* WALTER) What did you think it was—a place that sold guards and dogs and barbed wire?

MAGEE   Then they chased you and you had the good sense to come here?

MARION   My daughter had the presence of mind.

MAGEE   She did the right thing, Mrs. Hollander.

WALTER   Sure—so you could tell them we're spies. My wife should not have to go through this. She's not a young woman.
(MARION *reacts surprised*)

MAGEE   On the one hand we want to protect you; on the other hand we want to protect the best interests of the United States.

WALTER   I always thought they went hand-in-hand.

MARION   I'm an old woman?

WALTER (*Affectionately*)   I didn't mean old. I meant young-old.

MAGEE   There's nothing to worry about.

WALTER   Sure, because I'm a caterer, not a spy. Creative catering—our specialty. We were the first to make bride-grooms out of potato salad.

MARION   He does lovely work, I'll say that for him.

WALTER   Last month we did a wedding reception. We did the bride's body in jello, her head in a very nice clam dip, with fruit punch spouting out of her throat. It was a class affair.

MAGEE   I should have this settled in a few days.

WALTER   What do you mean? What do you think I'm gonna do—live here?

MAGEE   It may require some effort, but we're going to show those Communists their police-state tactics don't work. I'll have Mr. Kilroy see if we have some spare cots.

WALTER   Cots? I will not sleep on a cot. I'm a dignified human being with a hernia.

MAGEE   It's an emergency, Mr. Hollander, and we'll try our best.

WALTER   I got a business. Sam Blackwell can't run the firm. He's the inside man. I'm the outside man. It requires personality.

KILROY   (*Entering abruptly*)   Mr. Hollander, was there some kind of a notebook in your suitcase back in the hotel, with some kind of party list in it?

WALTER   No . . . oh, yes. The Levine wedding estimate.

KILROY   What is that?

WALTER   The Levine wedding—how many from the bride's side, how many from the groom's side, how much roast beef, how much grapefruit.

21

KILROY The Communist police say they've been working on it and they've broken the code.

WALTER What code?

KILROY Supply information and troop movements.

WALTER Troop movements? That's the Levines and the Wassermans. There's more Levines because she's paying for the wedding and they eat like an army, but they're civilians.

MAGEE It's that damn Krojack trying to frame you.

WALTER I can't stay here. This is the height of the season. I got weddings coming up, I got receptions, I got coming-out parties. Sam Blackwell can't handle it by himself. He lacks my charm.

MARION So he'll have his son come in and help out. He's over twenty-one.

WALTER His son? Who's gonna dress him?

MAGEE Your business can manage for a few days.

WALTER You think so? And, now, if you'll excuse me, I'm going to America. Where's my hat?
(*He starts toward the door*)

MARION Mr. Magee, what do you think's going to happen?

WALTER Let them capture me. I'm a caterer.

KILROY This is preposterous.
(*He exits*)

WALTER They want information? I'll tell them how to make grapefruit sections.
(*He continues walking toward the door*)

MAGEE Mr. Hollander, you can't go out there.

MARION (*Calling his bluff*) Let him go out there. Go ahead, big shot. We'll be in here if you want us. Go ahead. There's the front door.

MAGEE (*Caught in the middle*) Now look . . .

WALTER (*To* MARION) Don't think I won't.

MARION Go ahead. Stop talking already and do it.

MAGEE Mrs. Hollander, don't start trouble.

WALTER You think I'm afraid of those guys?

MARION No. Why should you be afraid? They're only secret police. They'll arrest you and torture you. What's to be afraid of?

WALTER You think I'm afraid to walk out?

MARION No. Go ahead, get brainwashed—in your case it'll probably help.

MAGEE I strongly urge you not to do anything rash . . .

23

MARION Let him go. Go ahead—go.

WALTER (*He gets to the door, pauses, and then comes quickly back to* MAGEE) Do you know if any of those guys belong to the Masons?
(MARION *waves her hand at him as if to say she knew he was bluffing.* SUSAN *now enters*)

SUSAN I've been hiding down in the basement.

MARION Mr. Magee, this is my daughter Susan. She was a Caesarian.

SUSAN How do you do, Mr. Magee?

MAGEE (*He is obviously taken with her looks. She is an off-beat, bohemian-looking girl but a stunner*) A-Axel Magee . . .

SUSAN Are we free to go home yet?

MAGEE (*A little tongue-tied*) Home?

WALTER Sure we're free to go home. Did you see what's doing out there thanks to this guy? We're liable to be stuck here three, four days.

MAGEE (*To* SUSAN) I'm awfully sorry for this inconvenience. I realize it's terrible.

SUSAN I think it's fun.

MAGEE (*Delighted at her attitude*) It can be fun. Some people might look upon this as an exciting experience.

WALTER   Some people bought Edsels.

SUSAN (*To her father*)   We could be worse off. This place is lovely.

WALTER   And what are we supposed to do about Seth?

MARION   Seth? Oh my God!

WALTER   Forgive her. In her panic she's completely forgotten that she gave birth twice.

MARION   I wasn't even worried about Seth. He's at camp.

WALTER   Camp ends tomorrow. If we're not back to let him in, what's going to happen? He'll be unsupervised. He'll live in the streets. He'll run amuck. He'll rape and loot. You know our son. He takes after your brother.

MARION   I just thought of something. Susan's getting married next week.

WALTER   That's right. I have a deposit on the hall.

MAGEE (*Obviously disappointed*)   Getting married, huh? I guess you're really anxious to get out of here.

SUSAN   That's a long story, Mr. Magee.

WALTER   Let's not discuss it. The date's been set.

MARION   Well, we may have to push the date back—so you better call the owner of the Renaissance Luau and get our deposit back.

25

WALTER (*To* SUSAN)   You better call Donald. He'll be worried sick.

SUSAN   I'll call. Mr. Magee, what's the longest anyone has ever had to stay here?

MAGEE (*Uncomfortably*)   Er, we gave asylum to a priest who's been living upstairs—er—awhile.

WALTER   What's awhile?

MAGEE   Oh, er, you know—awhile.

MARION   How long?

MAGEE (*After a lot of squirming*)   Six years.

WALTER (*Dumbstruck*)   Six years? I said, let's go to Atlantic Beach—we'll swim, we'll play pinochle—no, her brother says, go to Europe . . . may he rest in peace . . .

MARION   He's not dead.

WALTER   He should *be!*

(*Blackout*)

It is later that night. MAGEE *is at a desk, while* KILROY *and* BURNS *are lugging a cot across the room. All are pretty exhausted.*

KILROY Oh . . . you could at least give us a hand, Mr. Magee.

MAGEE Look, Mr. Kilroy. I've been on the phone for the past six hours with Washington, with their Embassy, with the UN. The whole picture has become clear to me now.

KILROY What whole picture?

MAGEE It's all over the American press. This morning the FBI captured this country's top secret agent. Adolph Lopert. The Gray Fox.

KILROY (*Setting the cot down*) The Gray Fox?

MAGEE One of their most brilliant spies. They caught him posing as a student at Berkeley. Apparently the Reds went after the first American tourists they could find, in retaliation.

KILROY Now I suppose they want to trade spies. Adolph Lopert for the Hollanders.

MAGEE Washington won't hear of it. They're outraged.

KILROY I wonder if that's the way it's going to be from now on. Every time we arrest one of their spies, they arrest one of our caterers.

BURNS I better help the chef. Mr. Hollander is driving him crazy. He hates European food.

KILROY Mr. Magee, are you aware that the Sultan of Bashir is due here Friday? I suggest we postpone it for a more auspicious moment.

MAGEE Nonsense, Mr. Kilroy. I should have this cleared up by Friday.

KILROY And if you don't?

MAGEE If I don't, business will go on as usual. *I'm* running this Embassy.
(SUSAN *enters*)

SUSAN Oh, Mr. Magee, may I please speak with you?

MAGEE Certainly. Mr. Kilroy, please. I'm sorry about your accommodations but we are jammed and it is temporary.
(*They carry the cot offstage*)

SUSAN Mr. Magee, I hope you're not upset by my parents.

MAGEE Upset?

SUSAN They're really sweet people; they just have their own way of expressing themselves. Don't let their form of communication throw you . . .

MAGEE Listen, you don't have to explain parents to me. I have two parents. I *had* two parents. My mother is in court trying to disown me.

SUSAN Mr. Kilroy explained to us that your father is Ambassador Magee.

MAGEE Did he also tell you if I don't make it here I'm finished?

SUSAN Oh. It's not that bad. Everybody makes mistakes. Every time I pick up the papers I read about another diplomatic crisis cropping up somewhere in the world.

MAGEE Have you noticed my name is in every article?

SUSAN Funny. You're just the opposite of Donald.

MAGEE Who's Donald?

SUSAN He's my fiancé. He's so confident and totally in command.

MAGEE Well, I'm confident too. Between major international blunders.

SUSAN Well, I don't know about anybody else, but I'm beginning to like it here.

MAGEE Gee, it's awfully sweet of you to take that attitude. I really appreciate it.

SUSAN I mean it. It's very exciting and romantic. Most people spend their whole lives without anything like this happening to them.

MAGEE   So your father keeps telling me.

SUSAN   Danger stimulates me. You know how many babies were born in England in World War II as a result of the blitz?

MAGEE   Well, if it's danger you want, take a look out there— (*Gesturing toward the window*) Must be two dozen professional killers.

SUSAN (*Looking*)   It's hard to see much . . .

MAGEE   Here. Knock off that light— You'll be able to see all the guards and secret police . . .
        (*He turns off the light; the moonlight streams through the window*)

SUSAN   Oh sure, look at them out there—they've got machine guns . . . Are you married, Mr. Magee?

MAGEE   One thing about my work—you don't usually get to meet any attractive American women.

SUSAN   Oh? Don't you have a girl friend, or someone back home?

MAGEE   Actually, my work has caused me to travel a lot. Suddenly. What do you do? Are you a model or an actress or something?

SUSAN   No. I danced. In the New York City Center Ballet. And I was a folk singer and I worked in a coffeehouse in Greenwich Village.

MAGEE   Waitress?

SUSAN   I repaired motorcycles. Right now my big interest is painting.

MAGEE   No kidding. I paint. You'd hate my work though, it's all very abstract. I stand back and splash oil all over everything and then I run all over it with my sneakers and I stick my lunch on it—in fact, my lunch came in second at a showing in Cape Cod.

SUSAN   I adore abstract art.

MAGEE   Really. I'm a big Jackson Pollack man. His drippings best express my mental state. After dinner if you're interested, I'll show you a little statue I made out of some old automobile parts and a bedpan.

SUSAN   I'd love it.

MAGEE   (*Coming close to her and speaking intimately*) Y'know, you're really very pretty.

SUSAN   Thank you.
        (*The* CHEF *comes onstage, seemingly agitated*)

CHEF   Forgive my intrusion, Mr. Magee, but I must know what is the decision for dinner.

MAGEE   What's the problem?

CHEF   It's him.

MAGEE   Who?

CHEF   Mr. Hollander.

SUSAN   (*To* MAGEE)   Be nice to him. I'll see you at dinner. (*She exits*)

CHEF   Every dish I name he says no.

MAGEE   Does he have any suggestion?

CHEF   Mr. Magee, we are four thousand miles from the United States, this is a Communist country, it's eight o'clock at night—where do you expect me to get Sara Lee coffee cake?
    (WALTER *enters the room*)

WALTER   (*Angrily*)   What kind of place is this?

CHEF   (*Running to him*)   Oysters.

WALTER   I will not eat oysters! They're alive when you eat them. I want my food dead—not sick, not wounded—dead.

CHEF   It's too late now to get anything new; take a very nice piece of veal.

WALTER   You must be joking.

CHEF   What's wrong with veal? My recipe is one of the great secrets of European cooking.

WALTER   Really? Let's keep it that way.

CHEF   (*Appealing*)   Mr. Magee. I have very little. If I had known. I couldn't get to the market, there were soldiers outside.

MAGEE Try and understand, Mr. Hollander, our menu here is particularly elaborate because we entertain guests from all over the world.

WALTER All I want is a plain piece of boiled chicken.
(MARION *comes onstage*)

MARION Walter, where did you go off to?

WALTER You know I can't get a meal here.

MARION I'll come in the kitchen and make you something.

WALTER Good.

CHEF Madam. How do you live with this man? Do you force-feed him?

MARION Don't worry, I know what he likes.

CHEF (*Becoming hysterical*) I warn you, madam, no one has ever been in my kitchen before. If you do anything to spoil the order of my spice rack, I don't know what I'll do. Do you hear me? I don't know what I'll do!
(*He storms out in a rage*)

WALTER It's good to know our food is being cooked by an outpatient.

MARION I spoke to Barney Silverman on the phone.

WALTER Did you tell him not to drive to Newark Airport with the station wagon because we may be six years late?

33

MAGEE   Mrs. Hollander—I wanted to speak to you about the phone. Naturally you're free to use it . . . If you could limit your calls to a few dozen.

WALTER   This is nothing for her. She has to alert everyone in Newark, individually, like Paul Revere.

MARION   I called the Kleins and they'll take care of Seth till we get back.

WALTER   You couldn't find a worse couple?

MARION   What's wrong with the Kleins?

WALTER   They have orgies.

MARION   How do you know?

WALTER   I catered one.
    (SUSAN *comes onstage, bringing with her a bewildered-looking* FATHER DROBNEY)

SUSAN   Mom, Dad. Hey, look who I met.

MAGEE   Father Drobney—what brings you down here!

DROBNEY   I heard so much commotion today and I met this young lady in the hall upstairs . . .

MAGEE   These are the Hollanders. They came here today in much the same way you did six years ago.

DROBNEY   Are you refugees?

WALTER   Refugees? You know what I paid for this shirt?

MARION   We were at the Vatican. We saw your boss. (*The phone rings. She and* MAGEE *go for it;* MAGEE *gets it first*) If it's for me I'm free to talk.

MAGEE (*Speaking into the phone*) Hello. Yes— I better take this inside. Excuse me a moment.
(*He hangs the phone up and exits*)

SUSAN   He's got a little tiny room on the top floor and he practically never leaves it.

WALTER   Don't you go crazy?

DROBNEY   I am a guest through the courtesy of your government, and I do not wish to make myself a nuisance.

MARION   Can't you ever leave here?

DROBNEY   Only if there is some drastic change in national policy. I have many friends who could help me to escape. But my duty is to return and some day lead my people once again.

MARION   But until you lead your people—you stay in your bedroom?

DROBNEY   In recent years I have developed a hobby and so it passes the lonely moments.

MARION   What do you do?

SUSAN   Father Drobney is a magician.

DROBNEY I've been practicing for years. Years.

MARION That's a wonderful hobby.

DROBNEY (*He takes a deck of cards from his pocket and holds it out to* WALTER) Pick a card—go ahead, any card . . . I'm not forcing!

WALTER It's all I needed!

SUSAN C'mon, Dad. Be a sport.

DROBNEY Go on—take any card.

MARION Walter. Don't be rude.
(WALTER *reluctantly picks a card*)

DROBNEY Jack of spades.

WALTER Wrong, five of diamonds.

DROBNEY Damn it! Sorry.
(*He crosses himself, looking up*)

SUSAN Father Drobney has all kinds of interesting things up there. Don't you, Father?

DROBNEY Doves—I have white doves. I raised them! I transform them before your eyes!

SUSAN Why don't you get some of your things—I'd love to see them!

DROBNEY (*Becoming excited*) Really? Would you?
(*He looks toward* WALTER)

36

MARION Of course he would, wouldn't you, Walter?

WALTER Of course, why do you think I had us trapped here.

DROBNEY I'll be down in a minute. An audience! An audience! I'll do the rings and my silk-handkerchief production and my vanishing billiard balls.

WALTER Terrific. It's the Ed Sullivan Show.

DROBNEY I'll be right down. (*He runs upstage; then as an afterthought he returns and addresses all*) Don't go away. (*He exits again*)

WALTER (*Sarcastically*) Don't go away.

SUSAN Imagine staying in your room and practicing magic for six years.

MARION What about us, Walter, what if the same thing happens to us?

WALTER Where do you compare? We're innocent tourists. He's a priest. I'm sure he could get out of here if he made some effort, but you know how it is with those guys. The one who suffers the most gets a promotion.

KILROY (*Coming onstage*) Mr. Hollander, I think we've solved your dinner problem.

WALTER What?

KILROY The chef is making you hare.

WALTER   What?

KILROY   Hare.

WALTER   What's hare?

SUSAN   Rabbit.

WALTER   Pardon me?

MARION   Hare is rabbit.

KILROY   It's the closest thing to chicken the chef could find.

WALTER   Rabbit?

KILROY   It's delicious.

WALTER   Bunny rabbit?

MARION   If you don't ask him, he eats what you put in front of him.

WALTER   You mean a rabbit? Like Peter Rabbit?

KILROY   If I told you it was chicken you wouldn't know the difference.

WALTER (*Exploding*)   I will not eat my furry friends! It's like eating squirrels . . . Look, can't you order out? There must be a Chinese restaurant in town.
      (FATHER DROBNEY *re-enters, overloaded with all kinds of colorful magical apparatus*)

DROBNEY I'm back.

WALTER He's back.

DROBNEY I could only carry the small things, but it's enough for the first few hours of the show.

MARION Er, how many hours does the show last?

DROBNEY Hold this.
(*He hands her a cane which turns into flowers upon her grasping it*)

WALTER (*Bemoaning to himself*) I want to go home.

DROBNEY (*Light bulb flashing in his hand*) I have dreamed of this moment for years. What miracle shall I start with?

MARION I don't know—can you walk on water?

WALTER (*Still moaning*) My son is twelve years old. I won't see him again till he's eighteen.

DROBNEY As you can observe, I have nothing up my robes.

MARION Isn't it wonderful, Walter—a tricky priest.

DROBNEY (*Pattering as he displays the apparatus*) I have nothing up my cylinder. I have nothing in my cage. Watch closely. I take this white dove and place it in here. Say the magic words . . . I remove this cylinder and where there was previously a dove—*voilà*. (*He looks and is surprised to find an empty cage*) Where's the rabbit? I had a rabbit in there. (*Becoming frantic*) Where's my rabbit?

39

CHEF (*Comes onstage holding a live rabbit and goes to*
WALTER)   How do you like it? Rare, medium, well-done?

DROBNEY   There's my rabbit!
(DROBNEY *lunges for the* CHEF, *who starts to run away.*
WALTER *begins running also, since the* CHEF *appears to
be headed in his direction.* MARION *and* SUSAN *are
ducking to avoid being trampled. Bedlam breaks loose
in the room.* MAGEE *comes onstage*)

MAGEE   Now just a minute. This is a United States Embassy,
and I mean to run it like one!
(*By now the room is a madhouse. Blackout*)

Lights come up on MAGEE, *who is talking on the phone. It
is now five days later.* MARION *is ironing in her robe, holding
her bag on her arm. The room is messier and various articles of
clothing are strewn over the furniture, either to dry or just
carelessly misplaced and forgotten.*

MAGEE Mr. Krojack, your charges of espionage are ridicu-
lous! They're tourists and we will not turn them over to
you. No, you will not wait them out. They've been here five
days and they're prepared to stay five years if necessary.
Don't threaten me. And don't threaten them. You know
you're only doing this because we captured Adolph Lopert,
your illustrious Gray Fox. I—hello! Hello!
  (*He hangs up in disgust*)

MARION (*Still ironing*) Boy, they're stinkers.

MAGEE Mrs. Hollander. Could you please remove this ironing board?

MARION Where should I iron? If I go in the kitchen the chef
starts to cry.

MAGEE (*Exasperated*) If everyone would please go to their
room.

MARION How much can a person keep locked up in a cloak-
room? Listen, I'm worried about Walter. First he wrote his

41

Congressman, and he got back a mimeographed form letter. Then he wrote his Senator, and he got back a mimeographed form letter, then he wrote our son, and he got back a mimeographed form letter—"I am okay. I am eating. I am getting plenty of rest. I will consider any suggestions you make. Your loving son, Seth."

MAGEE That's because he writes him three letters a day. He worries about that boy too much. There's no need for your husband to send him food from Europe. Please remove that ironing board.
(*She begins to fold the ironing board.* WALTER *walks across the stage in his robe and underwear*)

MARION Hello, Walter. (WALTER *ignores her and exits*) You see that. I said, "Hello, Walter." You see the look he gave me? (*She begins to follow after him, carrying her ironing board*) Hello, grouch.

MAGEE (*He goes after her as* KILROY *comes onstage*) Mrs. Hol—

KILROY (*Interrupting*) He should be here any minute.

MAGEE Who should?

KILROY The Sultan of Bashir. Or did you forget?

MAGEE The Sultan? Wasn't that called off?

KILROY I suggested a postponement but you assured everyone you would have matters settled and that business would proceed as usual.

MAGEE Oh, hell. Let me think.

KILROY You know the Sultan is a dictator and a very temperamental man. Any little ripple could hurt your father's oil deal, and I'd hate to be in your shoes if that happens.
(*He exits*)

MAGEE Maybe I can still call him and delay it.
(*He exits after* KILROY. WALTER *and* MARION *come onstage*)

WALTER I got a telegram this morning. Sam Blackwell caters a sweet-sixteen party.

MARION I don't want to hear.

WALTER He gets a special price on the meats . . .

MARION I'm not interested.

WALTER He doesn't use our regular guy, ya hear? Tries to buy cheap.

MARION I'm not listening.

WALTER Four guests go home that night and what happens? They get food poisoning.

MARION Oh my God . . .

WALTER They're in the hospital. Because he looked for bargains.

MARION I'll bet they're suing . . .

WALTER   Aha! Now you wanna hear!

MARION   Are they?

WALTER   I don't want to tell you—you're not interested.

MARION   Tell me!

WALTER   No, listen, you're not interested, why should I tell
you . . .

MARION   Tell me!

WALTER   (Hands over ears, he starts to sing) Hmmm,
hmmm, hmmm . . . "A foggy day in London town . . . It
had me low—"

MARION   Walter. You know what you are? You are a sadist.

WALTER   Why? A minute ago you weren't interested.

MARION   I'm not interested.

WALTER   You're not? Good. (He starts to sing again) "A
foggy day . . ."

MARION   Grouch! Are you gonna answer me?

WALTER   Are they suing? Is that what you asked? No, they're
not suing. They're not suing. We're suing them for low
resistance to tainted meat.

MARION   Walter—

44

Lou Jacobi and Kay Medford as WALTER and MARION
HOLLANDER.

WALTER Of course they're suing. What do you expect from poisoned people?

MARION Oh my God!

WALTER If I could get Sam Blackwell here, I'd crush his head!

MARION Be thankful nobody died.

WALTER Yes, Marion. We're thinking of making that our slogan.
(FATHER DROBNEY *comes onstage, struggling to get out of a strait jacket*)

DROBNEY Excuse me. Will someone help me out of this?

WALTER Not now with the magic tricks.

DROBNEY I don't know how Houdini used to get out of this.

MARION (*Going to* DROBNEY's *aid*) Don't pay any attention to him, Father. I think it's marvelous a man of the cloth has a hobby besides just God.

WALTER A person builds a catering firm for twenty years, he goes away and leaves his partner in charge. He begins poisoning customers. I'm working with Lucrezia Borgia!

DROBNEY Faith in the Lord, my son.

WALTER I have faith in the Lord, Father, if he can hear me now—please crush Sam Blackwell's head.
(*The phone rings.* MARION *answers it*)

45

MARION Hello? What? . . . Yes? . . . No, hold it. (*To* WAL-
TER) It's New Jersey for you. Must be Sam Blackwell. Be
nice. We all make mistakes.

> (*She hands* WALTER *the phone as she proceeds to help*
> DROBNEY *struggle out of his strait jacket. Throughout
> the following she and* DROBNEY *get entangled and drop
> to the floor. Her hairpiece comes off*)

WALTER Hello? Yes . . . Yes, this is he. Yes, go ahead.
Hello, cretin. How are you, cretin? Poison any more people, cretin? How many? Wonderful. Keep up the good
work. (*To* MARION *and* DROBNEY) Two more keeled over—
they're dropping like flies. Murderer. Murderer . . . I can't
hear you. Talk louder, murderer . . . Well, what did the
lawyer say? Oh, really? He feels they have a case, eh?
Blackwell, when I get back to the States, I'm going to rent
a car and run you over, you understand? Hello? . . . Murderer, I can't hear you, Blackwell—louder— Overseas Op-
erator, I can't hear the murderer. Blackwell, you're finished
as a caterer—you've mixed your last fruit compote!

> (*By now* MARION *and* DROBNEY *are a completely en-
> tangled blob on the floor.* WALTER *is on the phone still
> yelling, and with the room in utter chaos, who enters
> but the* SULTAN OF BASHIR *and his veiled wife. He is a
> huge imposing desert chieftain, in full robes, with
> dark glasses and beard.* BURNS *enters with him*)

BURNS Mr. Magee—His Majesty has arrived . . . (*He sees
the situation*) Oh, my God! Mr. Magee! Mr. Magee!

> (BURNS *runs offstage to get* MAGEE. *The* SULTAN *stares
> face-to-face with* WALTER, *who has just hung up the
> phone. The* SULTAN *also sees* MARION *and* FATHER

DROBNEY *on the floor, the priest still in his strait jacket*)

WALTER   What have we got here? Lawrence of Arabia.

MARION   (*Extricating herself, curtsying*)   How do you do, Sultan?

WALTER   Sultan? You know him?

MARION   Are you ignorant? It's the Sultan of Bashir.

WALTER   What do you do? Hang around the UN Building, picking up Arabs?

SULTAN   I am His Royal Majesty, Ruler of the People of Bashir. I am here to see Ambassador Magee.

MARION   How do you do?

SULTAN   This is my wife.

MARION   (*To the* SULTAN's *wife*)   Hello. Can I take your veil?

WALTER   I'm Walter Hollander, from New Jersey. (DROBNEY *tries wrenching free from his strait jacket, but fails*) Drobney, you'll have a heart attack—you're not a young man.

DROBNEY   (*Embarrassed, he thrashes out of the room and up the stairs*)   Excuse me, Your Majesty.

SULTAN   I am a guest of Ambassador Magee's.

MARION (*Trying to be polite*) I hope you didn't have any trouble getting by all those soldiers around the Embassy. Walter and I are wanted.

WALTER (*Struck by a thought*) I know where I read about the Sultan of Bashir recently—didn't you fellas put down an uprising?

SULTAN Eh?

WALTER Didn't you have some kind of revolution or something?

SULTAN Where's the Ambassador?

WALTER (*Not really unfriendly*) Sure . . . you killed all those workers . . . I read about it. That wasn't nice what you did to those people—they were protesting peacefully.

SULTAN There are two sides to that affair, my friend.

WALTER (*Still innocently enough*) What kind of two sides? A few poor workers go on strike. You gotta shoot 'em?

SULTAN If you could see them. They are vermin. There's no other way to teach them.
     (WALTER *listens with growing irritation*)

MARION Er, Walter—what are you talking about something you know nothing about.

WALTER (*Becoming annoyed*) I don't know politics? What's the matter with you? Don't you read the papers? This guy executes his people like you use your Charge-A-Plate.

MARION You're in a bad mood.

SULTAN I did not come here to be received by a pair of dogs. Where is the Ambassador?

WALTER (*Dealing this square into the* SULTAN's *face*) I always read things in the papers and I get frustrated because being a little shot from New Jersey I never get a chance to express my opinion to a real big shot.

MARION No one asked you.
(MAGEE *enters just in time to prevent what might have turned into a pushing match*)

MAGEE Your Majesty—forgive us.

SULTAN I will not stay here unless I receive an apology from your government.

MAGEE Mr. Hollander, leave this room at once.

WALTER (*To the* SULTAN) What's your trouble, Aladdin?

MARION Walter, you're in a very bad mood this morning. Let's go.

WALTER I live here. I'm not going any place. I pay taxes. Why, 'cause this bum has some oil wells?

MAGEE Your Majesty, please come inside.

SULTAN You are an insolent swine!

WALTER I'll hit him a shot in the chops, they'll have to bandage him in his own sheets!

SULTAN Don't threaten me, you pig!

WALTER (*To* MAGEE) What is this guy doing here anyway?

MAGEE That's none of your business.

WALTER This is my business. I pay taxes. This building is rented with my money.

MARION Walter, butt out.

WALTER I don't like the idea of my government doing business with this guy.

MAGEE Mr. Hollander, that's something for the government to decide.

WALTER I am the government!

MARION Listen to him. He's the government.

WALTER What do you think the government is? It's little people like you and me! (*He then considers her in her robe*) Well, maybe not you.

SULTAN I have never been insulted in such a manner.

MAGEE Your Majesty, I beg your forgiveness.

WALTER Take a walk, fatso! That's how this country gets into trouble. Dealing with guys like him!

MARION In your opinion.

WALTER   Yeah. Read Walter Lippmann!

SULTAN   I did not come here to be humiliated. Relations between us are at an end.
(*He and his wife begin to exit in a huff*)

MAGEE (*Follows placatingly*)   Your Majesty! . . .
(*They go offstage,* MAGEE *in pursuit*)

WALTER   And every time you bring somebody into this house
who's a bum like him—they get the same. Come on, Marion.
(*He walks off in the opposite direction, proudly*)

MARION (*Following* WALTER *off, she takes a parting shot at
him*)   For a man who cheats on his income tax, you're certainly a big shot.
(*Blackout*)

SCENE 4

As lights come on, MAGEE *is on the phone. It is later that night. As usual,* MAGEE *is having a hard time of it.*

MAGEE   Dad. Dad. It wasn't my fault. Mr. Hollander insulted him. But, Dad, you said it would look bad for the family image if you put Mr. Kilroy in charge. (KILROY *enters*) Dad? Yes, Dad. Yes, sir. Good-bye.

KILROY   I'll start right away to see if I can arrange a spy trade. Hard luck, Magee, but those are the breaks.
   (*He exits.* SUSAN *comes onstage*)

SUSAN   Hi, Axel. I brought you a drink. I thought you might need one.

MAGEE   Why? Why does it always happen? What do I do? I'll kill myself—that's it—I'm gonna kill myself . . .

SUSAN   Axel, what happened?

MAGEE   I'm a failure. I'm thirty years old and a failure—not just a *little* failure, I'm a *big* failure, like the World's Fair.

SUSAN   Have a drink.

MAGEE   I've been relieved of my command by Kilroy and the United States Weather Bureau has declared me a disaster area.

SUSAN   Your job really means a lot to you, doesn't it?

MAGEE I guess it's hard to understand. It's all I've been brought up to think of.

SUSAN I understand. It's not easy to be the son of a famous person.

MAGEE Susan. Do you know that when I was ten years old and I did something wrong, my mother used to hit me with a copy of *Time* magazine with my father's picture on the cover?

SUSAN Oh, Axel. I don't find you a failure. Maybe you're just in the wrong field. Maybe in some other business you'd be a genius.

MAGEE Sure, if there was such a thing as the failure business—I'd have chain stores. What does your fiancé do?

SUSAN He's a lawyer.

MAGEE I know it's none of my business, but you don't seem wildly enthused over the prospect of getting married.

SUSAN I'm not getting married. I haven't told my parents yet but I have told Donald. Donald's bright and *very* handsome but—not for me.

MAGEE (*Suddenly heartened*) I see. Ahem. I guess your father will be disappointed.

SUSAN Oh, he's going to have a stroke. He adores Donald. And compared to the kind of boys I almost married, Donald's the answer to a father's prayer.

MAGEE Have you almost married often?

SUSAN A few times—and always the type that would turn my father's hair gray. A manic-depressive jazz musician, a draft-dodger, and a defrocked priest.

MAGEE Boy, you must really hate the suburbs.

SUSAN If I tie myself down for life I want someone—

MAGEE Stable and successful.

SUSAN No. I want a little action.

MAGEE (*Quick to agree*) That's what I mean. You don't want anything too stable or successful.

SUSAN The truth is you never know what you want. You think you want a certain type and then you meet somebody who has nothing of what you want, and for some unexplainable reason you fall in love with him.

MAGEE I know. I once wrote a poem about that.

SUSAN A poem? Axel, you're a latent creator. Is the place still heavily surrounded?

MAGEE Yes. You wanna see?
(*He turns out the light. Suddenly the mood is romantic*)

SUSAN (*Peering out the window*) Look at all those stars. You can see the Dipper, see?

(*As she looks,* MAGEE *is sneaking up behind her, meaning to grab and kiss her. She turns abruptly and he rapidly tries to fake being casual by leaning against the office door. Unfortunately, the door is wide open and his attempt to lean on it sends him hurtling out of the room. He re-enters, trying to appear nonchalant*)

MAGEE   Sorry. Um, the air is so clear this time of year.

SUSAN (*Turning to the window*)   I love fall. It's such an exciting time of year. It's the start of everything.

MAGEE (*Beginning to creep up behind her for another try*) I like winter. Because I love to ski.

SUSAN   I've never gone skiing but I'm mad for the idea.

MAGEE   Maybe some day when all this gets worked out I could take you skiing. I know you'd love it. It's very romantic. I broke my pelvis once.
(*Realizing what he said he buries his face in his hands*)

SUSAN   Well, it's very late. I better go to bed. Good-night, Axel. It was fun talking to you.

MAGEE   Thanks for the—drink—
(*Suddenly he grabs her and tries to kiss her. They both topple over the sofa and she splatters on the floor*)

SUSAN   Whaaa . . .

MAGEE   I'm sorry! Are you okay?

SUSAN (*Getting up and backing away from this maniac*)   I better go now.

MAGEE (*Trying to go to her and help her*)   Please forgive me. I . . . I . . .

SUSAN (*Running for her life*)   Excuse me.

MAGEE   I'm awfully sorry. Are you all right?

SUSAN   I'm okay. Good-night.
(*She bolts up the stairs*)

MAGEE   Good-night. I'm sorry—I . . . DAMMIT! Why can't I do anything right! (*He kicks the table out of anger and succeeds only in hurting his toe*) Eoowwwww!
(*He dances wildly on one foot, in pain. Blackout*)

The lights come up on WALTER. *He is on the phone and radiates excitement.*

WALTER Son, we'll be home tonight. That's right, boy, we're being traded for a Communist spy. A big spy. Oh, it's a terrific thing. You'll read about it in the papers. (MARION *enters, dressed for travel, lugging all the family suitcases*) Is there anything you want us to bring you? Anything from here? (*To* MARION) He wants us to take some pictures! (*Back into the phone*) Cretin. We'll see you later and don't forget to thank Mrs. Klein. (*He hangs up*) I called Donald last night.

MARION *You* called Donald? Don't you think that's Susan's business?

WALTER Ah, I feel she neglects him. Besides, I want to establish good relations with my future son-in-law.

MARION What'd he say?

WALTER He wasn't home. My future attorney was in court . . . suing a slum landlord. The boy is a poet.

MARION I called Barney Silverman—he rented the station wagon again.

WALTER Good, on the way home he can drop me at work.

MARION You're not coming home first?

WALTER What for?

MARION You're going directly from Europe to work?

WALTER Why not?

MARION Are you crazy?

WALTER I'll help with the unpacking when I come home at seven.

MARION You haven't seen our apartment in six weeks . . .

WALTER Who was there to change it?

MARION A man hasn't seen his apartment in six weeks—he's going to work first?

WALTER It's a Thursday. I always work Thursday.

MARION The business can't wait another day?

WALTER (*Exiting*) What do you care?

MARION (*Following him offstage*) Walter, if I cash in our Mutual Funds, will you see a psychiatrist?
      (SUSAN *enters carrying a suitcase.* MAGEE *comes on-stage and takes the suitcase from her*)

MAGEE All packed?

SUSAN It was clever of Mr. Kilroy to arrange this spy exchange, Axel.

MAGEE Yes, he's very efficient. He's already lined up a big reception for the Sultan of Bashir this weekend and I'm sure he'll smooth that situation over as quickly as he did this. I guess some just have the knack.

SUSAN I'd still rather be you.

MAGEE I'm going to miss you, Susan.

SUSAN If you're ever in Newark . . .

MAGEE At the rate I'm going it could happen.

SUSAN Axel, I'm sorry about the other night.

MAGEE *You're* sorry?

SUSAN I'm sorry I got so shaken up. It was something I wanted you to do and when you did it I got shaken up.

MAGEE I wish we could have spent some time together.

SUSAN So do I. Well—at least you'll still have your job.

MAGEE Yeah.
(MARION *and* WALTER *enter, both carrying more luggage*)

MARION I can't understand you—they've been so nice to us here, how can you stick their towels in your suitcase?

WALTER It's habit. I was a deprived child.

MARION You sure it's safe to go out there?

MAGEE It's all been carefully worked out. Mr. Krojack will accompany you to the plane.

MARION Did you take your hair dryer out of Mr. Burns' office?
(*Enter* FATHER DROBNEY *with the* CHEF)

DROBNEY We came to say good-bye and to wish you good luck.

CHEF (*Obviously insincere*) Yes. It's a pity you're leaving.

WALTER (*Joshing him*) If you ever need a job, Chef, I could probably get you one at Chock Full O'Nuts.

CHEF I may as well tell you, Mr. Hollander, the veal you had last night was eel. And you cleaned your plate.

WALTER Look in the vase next to the dining-room table.
(*Outraged, the* CHEF *exits*)

DROBNEY Bless you all. You have made my life richer. (DROBNEY *appears to want to shake hands, but offers a card instead.* WALTER *picks one, good-naturedly*) Five of diamonds.

WALTER (*Amazed*) Right. (*He then grabs the deck from* DROBNEY *to examine them*) They're all five of diamonds.
(DROBNEY *exits.* KILROY *comes onstage*)

KILROY Mr. Krojack has arrived.
(*Enter* KROJACK)

KROJACK So, we finally meet face-to-face.

WALTER We don't hold a grudge.

MARION Sure—you can't with the H-bomb.

WALTER Let bygones be bygones.

KROJACK (*Booming*) Criminals against the State!

MARION Take it easy, mister, you'll live longer.

KROJACK Only for Adolph Lopert, the Gray Fox, would our government do this.

KILROY Mr. Magee, will you check and see that the Hollanders haven't left anything?

MAGEE I think there's a couple of cartons upstairs.
(*He and* SUSAN *go offstage*)

MARION (*Making a last-minute rummage through her purse*) I better make sure Walter took his passport. Wouldn't it be a scream if you had to spend the rest of your life on Ellis Island?
(MARION *exits.* BURNS *comes onstage*)

BURNS Mr. Kilroy, there's a phone call for you and it's urgent. Why don't you take it inside where it's private?
(BURNS *exits with* KILROY, *leaving* KROJACK *and* WALTER *alone, face-to-face. The air is ridden with tension.* WALTER *finally waves his finger at* KROJACK)

KROJACK (*With ugliness*) If I could have my way—you and all those like you would hang in the public square as an example to all enemies of the State.

WALTER Krojack, when was the last time you called up a girl and she said "Yes"?

KROJACK I have men who worked with the Gestapo during the war. One hour at their disposal and you would tell everything.

WALTER Tell what? Who's got what to tell?

KROJACK Admit it! You are a filthy American spy!

WALTER Who? What?

KROJACK (*Pressing him*) Admit it!

WALTER Who?

KROJACK (*Relentlessly*) Admit it!

WALTER What?

KROJACK (*Screaming*) Admit it!

WALTER (*Having put up with enough*) Okay! I admit it! If it makes you happy, I admit it! I'm not a caterer. I'm not from New Jersey. She's not my wife, she's a U-boat commander. You happy? You're supposed to be so clever— you're nothing! This was my easiest caper since the Kowalski wedding!

KROJACK (*Uncontrollably enraged, he starts toward* WALTER) I will kill you myself!

WALTER (*Brandishing his hand to "chop"*) I wouldn't try

anything if I were you. We're all trained in karate, you know—Ah!— (*He jumps into a position*) Ahh— (*He jumps again, assuming another position*) Ahh—
  (*He chops his hand down on the coffee table to demonstrate his strength, and surprises himself and* KROJACK *by cracking the table in two*)

KROJACK If my hands were not tied by stupid red tape, I would have my men come in here and drag you out.

WALTER It riles you, doesn't it? You like to bully people, don't you? Wait'll I get back home and tell the newspapers how we made monkeys out of you. You'll be the laughing stock of the secret police. I wouldn't be surprised if they take away your disguise kit.

KROJACK (*Taunted, he goes for* WALTER *again*) You will die. I will see to it. If I must do it with my bare hands.

WALTER (*Thrusting his hand in his own jacket pocket and faking that he has a gun*) Don't make a move or I'll blow you to pieces.

KROJACK You're bluffing.

WALTER Oh, yeah, big shot?
  (*Having been carried away by the situation,* WALTER *pulls his hand out of his pocket. Pointing his finger as though it were a gun, he sticks it up against* KROJACK's *face*)

KROJACK Ha Ha. You fool. That's a finger!

WALTER   It may look like a finger—but it's a flesh-colored .45 with two joints, a knuckle, and a little hair.
> (*He puts it back in his pocket*)

KROJACK   Idiot!
> (MARION *enters, followed by* SUSAN *and* MAGEE *carrying the last pieces of luggage*)

MARION   Walter, I'm ready to go.

WALTER   (*Sweating, but one up on* KROJACK)   Me too. You got everything?

KROJACK   I had finally convinced the authorities to let me use my own methods of dealing with you. This trade has cheated me out of that and has saved your lives. But some day we will meet again.
> (*He and* WALTER *stand face-to-face, adversaries.* KIL-ROY *enters, white-faced*)

KILROY   The deal is off.

MAGEE   What?

KILROY   I have just received word from our Intelligence. Adolph Lopert is dead.

KROJACK   (*Stunned*)   Dead?

KILROY   He has hung himself in his cell.

KROJACK   (*In disbelief*)   Dead? Adolph Lopert is *dead*?

64

WALTER (*Also stunned*) He's dead? He's not alive? He's dead? (*As he looks at the vicious* KROJACK) Oh boy, am I in trouble.

KROJACK The Gray Fox dies by his own hand. I must go back to my office immediately. (*To* WALTER) So we *shall* meet again—and soon.
      (*He exits, followed by* KILROY, *who goes to show him out*)

MARION Walter. What are we going to do?

WALTER (*Shaky*) We're not going home?

MAGEE I—guess not . . .

WALTER (*Musing, glassy-eyed*) He had to pick today to hang himself. He couldn't wait till the weekend? It's a holiday weekend.

MARION See, and you wanted to rush to work. I better call Barney Silverman.

WALTER I'm getting drowsy.

MARION Drowsy?

WALTER I already took a Dramamine. (*They all look at him*) It's a half hour before takeoff! They caught him seven days ago, he had all this time, he had to pick today! And this morning yet.

MARION It's five A.M. there—he did it before breakfast. See how important it is to eat? Well, we better unpack.

WALTER I'll call Seth and tell him to go ahead with his application to the Foster Parents' home.
(*Exit* WALTER)

SUSAN (*Musing*) What makes a man kill himself?

MARION What do you expect from a Gray Fox. Is that a name for a grown-up person?
(*She goes offstage dejectedly with the luggage*)

SUSAN (*Alone with* MAGEE) Well, you wanted us to spend more time together.
(*They stare at one another with mixed feelings, then he goes to her and kisses her. She responds. In the midst,* WALTER *re-enters*)

WALTER Magee, do you think it's possible . . . Uhh—oh boy—oh boy . . . Marion, come quickly—she's kissing the failure!
(*Curtain*)

Act Two

Anthony Roberts, Anita Gillette, and Dick Libertini as
AXEL MAGEE, SUSAN HOLLANDER, and FATHER DROBNEY.

The lights come up on an empty stage. FATHER DROBNEY *once again comes downstairs and addresses the audience.*

DROBNEY   While you were out smoking, the Hollanders have been living here nearly two weeks now and everyone is really feeling the strain. Mrs. Hollander has nothing to do and so she goes around all day cleaning the Embassy.
  (*Enter* MARION *holding a feather duster*)

MARION (*As she dusts*)   I've waxed every floor in the house today twice. Even the rooms with wall-to-wall carpeting.
  (*She exits*)

DROBNEY   It's nice to be clean but a lot of floor wax is a dangerous thing.
  (*Enter* KILROY, *his arm in a sling, rapidly crossing the stage*)

KILROY   Goddamn living-room floor.
  (*He exits*)

DROBNEY   Susan and Magee feel a different kind of strain.
  (*Enter* SUSAN *and* MAGEE)

SUSAN (*In love*)   I wish there was someplace we could go to be alone.

MAGEE   Your father watches us like a hawk. Last night when he thought we were going to meet in the dining room he squatted motionless, put a throw-pillow on his lap, and pretended to be a chair.

SUSAN You're kidding!

MAGEE No! I sat on him!
    (*They exit*)

DROBNEY If Mr. Hollander's behavior seems a little extreme, it's only because he is a man torn between a failing business, a failing future son-in-law, and a twelve-year-old boy that he misses very much.
    (*Enter* WALTER, *composing a letter*)

WALTER Dear Seth, don't forget to dress warmly. And eat slowly. Chew your food carefully, and go to bed early, and stay away from women. See what happened to me?
    (*Exit* WALTER)

DROBNEY After thinking it over very carefully and weighing the pros and cons, I had a long talk with Mrs. Hollander and Susan, about the only way to see their home again. ESCAPE!
    (MARION *and* SUSAN *steal on from opposite upstage entrances*)

MARION Did Father Drobney speak to you about an escape?

SUSAN Yes. I think it's a wonderful idea!

MARION Did you suggest it to Mr. Magee?

SUSAN Not yet. I want to wait till the moment's right. Did you suggest it to Daddy?

MARION I wouldn't dare. You know how he hates to take me any place.

(They exit separately. MAGEE *enters, then looks out the window)*

DROBNEY   Hello, Magee.

MAGEE   Hello, Father. I didn't want to alarm anybody but I don't like what's happening out there. This morning there were just a few pickets in front of the building. The number's been growing and now there's dozens. And a lot of them look too old to be students to me.

DROBNEY   Ah, yes, I see. Some are not students. Some are Communist agitators.

MAGEE   Well, just how ominous are those anti-Hollander signs they're carrying?

DROBNEY   Is there a safe place to hide the Hollanders in the event of serious rioting?

MAGEE   Serious rioting? What do you have in mind?

DROBNEY   Stoning, looting, fires.

MAGEE   Stoning, looting, fires. My life is like the Old Testament. The only thing I've been able to avoid so far is locusts.

DROBNEY   The Hollanders are enemies of the State. Krojack has many followers who will stop at nothing. If they choose to they will find a way to come in here and get the Hollanders out.
   (He starts to exit)

MAGEE *(Following him)*   See, Kilroy doesn't understand the danger of these things. He lacks my vast experience getting stoned and spit at. I better call my father direct and let him know there may be trouble.

(WALTER *and* MARION *enter just as* MAGEE *is about to exit*)

WALTER   I want to speak to you.

MAGEE   Later, Mr. Hollander.
(*He exits*)

WALTER   All of a sudden it's good-bye successful lawyer, hello psychotic diplomat!

MARION   It's her own life, Walter. She's twenty-three.

WALTER   Who says it's not her own life. I just want her to do the right thing, that's all . . .

MARION   So.

WALTER   So, what I tell her is the right thing. This guy is what we used to call in the poolroom, a loser!

MARION   He's a Yale graduate.

WALTER   Yale makes mistakes too.

MARION   Walter, don't get involved.

WALTER   This is the worst prospect she's ever had. I like even the draft dodger she was going with better because he at least was a success—he beat the draft—something!

MARION   May I remind you that when I married you, your future didn't look too secure.

WALTER   That's different—where do you compare. I have a *joie de vivre*.

MARION   What good is security if she's not happy?

WALTER   Where does happy come into this? I'm talking about marriage! When you get married you give up happiness! All of a sudden Donald can't make her happy? He's an attorney—he has court cases, he'll fill out briefs, there's mortgages, there's litigation—it's romantic.
  (*He removes some letters from his jacket pocket and goes to the stove*)

MARION   She was always a little lukewarm about Donald, I felt . . . I didn't want to say anything. Hey, what are you doing with the stove?

WALTER   This is a stove?

MARION   It's a procelain-tiled stove. You think Europe has central heating?

WALTER   I've been mailing letters in it.
  (*He puts the letters back in his pocket dejectedly*)

MARION   (*Hearing increased noise from outside the window*) What is that? That must be those pickets outside.
  (*She goes to the window to look*)

WALTER   Marion, be careful. I thought there was only a few . . .

MARION Walter, look what's doing out there—it's a regular demonstration. Oh my God! They have a cloth dummy that looks like you and they're burning it.
(The noise from outside begins building)

WALTER Maybe they think I'm a football coach.

MARION Walter, this is not a joking matter. They got big black ugly signs with our names on them.
(The noise is very loud now)

WALTER Sticks and stones will break my bones but names will never harm me.

MARION Walter, they have sticks and stones!

WALTER Come away from the window!
(Three shots coming from another part of the Embassy are heard)

MARION What was that?
(SUSAN runs in, frantic)

SUSAN *(Yelling to be heard above the noise)* They're shooting and throwing rocks through the windows! Mr. Kilroy got hit in the head with a brick. He's lying on the hall floor muttering something about aviation.

WALTER Don't panic. Everybody remain *calm!* *(Two gunshots come from the window)* Okay—now you can panic!

SUSAN Duck! It's a riot!
(They all hide behind the sofa, and under tables)

WALTER (*From the floor*) Magee! Magee! Magee! Come quickly! We have your usual riot!

MARION (*Under the table*) Walter, what are we going to do?

WALTER Try not to get shot.
(*More gunshots ring out*)

MARION Walter—maybe if you went outside and addressed them.

WALTER I said let's go to Atlantic Beach—we'll swim, we'll play pinochle—
(MAGEE *bursts in, crouching to avoid being shot. Two more gunshots are heard and a ticking time bomb comes through the window and lands on the floor*)

MAGEE Is everybody all right?

SUSAN Yes, are you?

WALTER (*Who has gone to the bomb and picked it up*) What's this?

MAGEE (*Noticing it in* WALTER's *hands*) Be careful! That's a time bomb!

WALTER A b-b-b-bo—
(WALTER *tosses it to* MAGEE, *who tosses it back to* WALTER, *in panic*)

MAGEE Don't put it down! The slightest tap could blow this place sky high!

WALTER   Agah-gah—don't anybody come near me!
(*The noise of the crowd subsides*)

MARION   They're running away.

MAGEE   Everybody out of the room. Quickly!

MARION   Walter, keep calm!

WALTER   I'm calm. Who's Walter?

MAGEE   I've had experience with these things. (*Trying to fix it*) If I can just dismantle it before it goes off . . .

WALTER   (*Sweating*) Dismantle. Dismantle.

SUSAN   Axel—be careful.

WALTER   My leg itches.

MARION   Where does it itch, Walter, I'll scratch it!

WALTER   Get out of the room—everybody!

MARION   What about you?

WALTER   Look out the window. You'll see me passing over the house any minute.

MARION   Come on, Susan, there's no sense in all of us getting torn limb-from-limb!

WALTER   Thanks, Marion.

MAGEE (*Letting out a huge sigh as he disconnects it*) There, it's dead. I did it.

WALTER (*Sighing*) My heart—my heart sounds like a discothèque.

MARION Who tells you to pick up strange objects?

WALTER That's how I met you!
(BURNS *enters*)

BURNS Has anyone been hurt?

MAGEE We're okay. What about everyone else?

BURNS Mr. Kilroy got hit in the head with a brick. He must have a concussion. He thinks he's the Wright brothers.

MAGEE (*To* BURNS) Wright brothers? Lodge a complaint at the ministry and report this to Washington. Tell them I tried reaching my father but he's on a yacht somewhere in the damn Caribbean.
(KILROY *comes onstage*)

KILROY (*Delirious*) Come quickly, Wilbur. I'm coming, Orville. I'm telling you, Wilbur, we can do it. Do what? Get those machines to fly. Orville, you're crazy. But so are you. Let's go down to Kitty Hawk Friday and put it in the air. We'll do it. Both of us. What if it doesn't work, Orville? Wilbur, we must try it and stop this arguing. Orville, you always were Mother's favorite.
(*He exits*)

MAGEE Mr. Burns, take Mr. Kilroy to his room and get the

doctor over here immediately. We may have to check him into a hospital.

WALTER   You better get him twin beds.
   (BURNS *exits*)

MARION   We better give Mr. Burns a hand, Walter. We may be next.
   (*They exit upstage*)

MAGEE   In the absence of my superiors I have no choice but to give myself a battlefield commission. Until further notice, I am in charge of this Embassy.

SUSAN   How exciting.

MAGEE   Now if I could think of what to do it would help.

SUSAN   I can.

MAGEE   What?

SUSAN   Axel—supposing my parents and I escape?

MAGEE   By escape, you mean what?

SUSAN   By escape I mean to leave here and show up in Newark.

MAGEE   Susan, you're nuts.

SUSAN   Axel, I've already spoken to Father Drobney about it and he says we can do it.

78

DON'T DRINK THE WATER

MAGEE   Father Drobney! The Holy Houdini? He can't get himself out of a strait jacket. What does he know?

SUSAN   He knows how to get us out of the country and he says it's a cinch. Axel, there's no other way!

MAGEE   Susan, why don't you get some rest and if you still feel the same way next year . . .

SUSAN   Why not? Give me one good reason.

MAGEE   Death, that's one good reason. If you think your father's uncomfortable here, wait'll you see him in front of a firing squad.

SUSAN   My parents are willing. We've already discussed it.

MAGEE   Then your parents should be locked up, and since they are locked up—we have nothing to talk about.

SUSAN   Axel, I'm serious.

MAGEE   (Hands over his ears, he begins to sing) "A foggy day . . ."

SUSAN   You have no imagination.

MAGEE   I have a wonderful imagination. Ten minutes after you try and escape I can picture Krojack wearing your father's shirt.

SUSAN   Axel, why can't we escape?

MAGEE   I just gave you a good reason. An escape requires

79

timing and coordination and good physical condition. Your father gets out of breath if I ask him to pass the salt.

SUSAN (*Convincingly*) Oh, Axel, for once in your life take the initiative. Don't let things happen to you. We'll do it together. That's what life is. A series of adventures you go through with someone you care about. We can do it, with you leading the way, your firm young jaw against the wind.

MAGEE Susan, have you been smoking the drapes?

SUSAN Let's tell my parents the idea.

MAGEE I thought you said they approved?

SUSAN My mother does. I thought you could tell Dad.

MAGEE Susan, I can't go through with this.

SUSAN (*Ignoring him*) Mother! Dad! Come quickly, Axel has something to tell you.

MAGEE Susan, let's discuss this.

SUSAN Axel, if we stay here it's just a question of time till another bomb comes through the window . . . You have no right to deny us a chance to save our lives.

MAGEE I'm not good at these things. I like a nice quiet evening at home.

SUSAN Axel, we can do it. The two of us—together.

MAGEE Be realistic, Susan. How would you get out of the building?

SUSAN Well . . . we could dig a tunnel.

MAGEE Dig a tunnel? Are you kidding? With our knowledge of engineering, we'd probably come up in the stove.

SUSAN All right, we could sneak out on the back of a laundry truck . . . I saw that in an old prison movie once.

MAGEE We don't send our laundry out any more. Your mother does it for the whole Embassy! No, you'd only have a chance, if, say, you were at a party, if you dressed as guests, mingled with the crowd, and left when everybody else leaves.

SUSAN Axel, that's brilliant!

MAGEE What is?

SUSAN Your idea! There's a party here Saturday night for the Sultan—we dress as guests, mingle, and walk right out!

MAGEE That's the craziest thing I ever heard!

SUSAN Axel, it's a stroke of genius.
     (MARION *and* WALTER *come onstage*)

WALTER What's so urgent? What does the failure want to tell us?

SUSAN Go ahead, Axel.

MAGEE (*Timid over broaching it*) Susan . . .

SUSAN (*In an urging tone*) Axel . . .

MAGEE (*Squirming before* WALTER) Eh—that was an awfully nasty bomb that came through the window before.

WALTER Did you notice that?

MAGEE (*Writhing*) Mr. Hollander, in view of circumstances, after careful consideration, I feel our situation calls for a little action.

WALTER What kind of action?

MAGEE Mr. Hollander, supposing you actually were trapped spies? What would you do?

WALTER I'd deny it and claim to be a caterer. What do you want from me?

MAGEE You read the papers—what do families do when they're caught behind the Berlin Wall and they want freedom desperately? So desperately—their lives depend on it.

WALTER What do they do? They escape. They go over walls or through tunnels, they forge passports, they go through roadblocks . . . It's been wonderful chatting with you, Magee. If you get any other hysterical notions be sure and call me.

MAGEE Mr. Hollander, it's the only way.

MARION Escape—what an interesting idea . . .

WALTER Magee, you're crazy. Do you know you're crazy? Years of insanity have made you crazy!

SUSAN Why not, Dad? It's better than being trapped here.

MARION Grouch, will you listen for a minute!

WALTER (*Hands to ears he begins humming*) "A foggy day in London town . . ."

MAGEE Mr. Hollander. This is a matter of life or death.

WALTER You picked the wrong person to talk to about an escape! I don't escape from places. That's not my field. I enter and I stay!

MAGEE It's wrong to reject an idea just because it sounds radical.

WALTER That's exactly it—it's radical—and when it comes to things like going over walls or forging passports or going through roadblocks, I'm a terrific conservative. I'm the John Birch of the escape world!

MARION Calm down. Will you please.

WALTER Marion, did you ever see a man with a hernia running from a tank!

SUSAN Dad. You read about it every day. Couples escape, husband escapes, lovers flee tyranny . . .

WALTER What you read is—couple *shot* escaping. Husband *shot* escaping. Lovers *killed* fleeing tyranny.

MARION You're a coward!

WALTER That's right, Mr. Anthony! If you wanted a hero you should have married Sergeant York!

MARION Do you want your daughter to grow up here for the rest of her life?

WALTER I'd rather she grew up here than grew up as an orphan. I'm funny that way, I can tolerate anybody's orphan but my own!

MARION (*Meaningfully*) You want your daughter to meet other eligible men, don't you?
(WALTER *stops in his tracks. He considers this and then looks at* MAGEE. *He ponders for a moment, and once again scrutinizes* MAGEE)

WALTER All right, let me hear it, let me hear this brilliant plot. I haven't had a good laugh in a long time—tell me the plan so I can go ha, ha.

MAGEE The night after tomorrow there's going to be a reception here.

WALTER Who's catering it?

MARION Will you let him finish?

MAGEE A big party in honor of the Sultan of Bashir. That night this house will be filled with dignitaries, men and

women from all nations, even from this country—you two
and Susan will dress as guests . . . Now then, you'll wait
in your room till midnight and when groups of guests leave,
you come downstairs, get your coats and go right out with
them.

MARION   It'll give you a chance to wear your dark-blue
mohair.

WALTER   I don't like my dark-blue mohair, it itches.

MARION   How can mohair itch? It's a soft fabric.

WALTER   Sue me, it itches!

MARION   Well, you'll have to wear a dark suit, I'm not going
to escape if you're not going to dress.

WALTER   We're not going any place!
    (DROBNEY *enters, interested by all this talk*)

MAGEE   Once outside we'll have the Embassy limousine
waiting and you're off.

WALTER   And if we did manage to get out of here, what
then?

DROBNEY   (*Joining right in*)   The rest is simple! My contacts
will see to it you are on your way home within hours.

MAGEE   Mr. Hollander, I appeal to you—for the safety of
everyone concerned, we must not procrastinate. Timing is
very important.

MARION   We'll see Seth again. I miss him so. By the way,

85

Walter, I didn't want to mention this because you'd get upset, but I got a letter from my brother—our apartment was robbed.

WALTER What!

MARION Burglars broke in. They stole the portable TV and all your shirts.

WALTER I'm cursed. I'm a cursed caterer. I'm trapped here and somewhere there's burglars running around with my initials on their cuffs.
(*He goes to the sofa, and accidentally sits on the bomb, which he then hands to* MAGEE *inadvertently*)

SUSAN Dad, let's go home.

DROBNEY (*Appeals to* WALTER) Mr. Hollander, I beg you. Magee's plan is a good one. You can trust him. I know he seems like a bungler, but he is actually bright and resourceful. He knows exactly what he is doing and you are in good hands.

WALTER (*Although he doesn't believe this, he figures finally, why not*) All right, we'll escape.

MAGEE Mr. Hollander, you have nothing to worry about. I'm in full control.
(*He tosses the supposedly dismantled bomb out the window and the stage is lit up with a huge explosion. When it clears,* DROBNEY *stares at* MAGEE *accusingly*)

DROBNEY (*To* MAGEE) You're a nut!
(*Blackout*)

86

The lights come up on FATHER DROBNEY *facing the audience.*

DROBNEY (*To audience*) The next few days were fraught with danger and intrigue. I made several phone calls to enlist the help of some of the most brilliant men in the underground. Unfortunately, they had all been captured. Magee worked around the clock devising an escape so complicated that only three people in the world understood it—and Magee was not one of them. On the morning of the day of escape, they reviewed the plan to make sure it was foolproof.
(WALTER *enters*)

WALTER (*Wearily*) It's a rotten plan. It won't work. Let's call it off.
(*Enter* MARION)

MARION We're not calling anything off.
(MAGEE *enters*)

MAGEE (*Obviously having gone through a lot preparing the Hollanders*) Now then, let's start from the top and go over the entire procedure again. Okay, Mr. Hollander, now who are you?

WALTER (*By rote*) I'm John Randall from Washington, D.C. I work in the Department of the Interior. I'm married and I have four children. I was born in Milwaukee,

Wisconsin, and went to school in California. I majored in agriculture and first entered government under Roosevelt. I drive a Chrysler Imperial; who's gonna ask me those questions!

MAGEE   In the event that you're stopped at any point your answers must be consistent.

WALTER   Ahhh, nobody's gonna believe I'm Sam Randall . . .

MAGEE *and* MARION   John Randall.

WALTER   John, Sam, I got such a headache.

MAGEE   What are you doing in Europe?

WALTER   (*Slowly, with an acid look at* MARION)   What am I doing in Europe? (*He pauses for a moment*) I'm making a tour of underdeveloped nations to initiate projects coping with the problems of soil conservation and erosion.

MARION   Very good.

WALTER   Don't "very good" me . . .

MARION   And I'm his lovely wife, Carmen. I'm also the former Miss Wisconsin of nineteen thirty-eight.

WALTER   If they believe that, we win the whole cold war. One look at those varicose veins and they'll think I'm smuggling road maps.

MAGEE   Where are you staying in town?

88

MARION   The Grand Hotel for one week, then we're flying to Malaysia.

MAGEE   All right, now what do you do when you leave here?

WALTER   Uh . . . uh.

MARION   At about midnight, when some of the other guests are leaving we casually say excuse me and leave with the largest group. Our chauffeur then drives us directly to the lobby of the Grand Hotel.

WALTER   Provided we haven't been stopped at the gate, identified, arrested, shot, beaten and tortured.

MARION   At the Grand Hotel we switch cars. A man will come up to me and say, "Those are extremely lovely earrings, my wife has a pair just like them." He will be our driver. We go with him.

MAGEE   Correct.

WALTER   What if a stranger happens to like her earrings? We'll wind up following him to Lapland.

MAGEE   What happens when he takes you to the railroad station?

WALTER   He takes us to the railroad station and a guy comes up to us, presumably not suspicious-looking, who says to me, "The grass is green"—which for my money, he might as well wear a neon sign saying, "I am a spy."

MAGEE   And what do you do?

89

WALTER We get on the train with him, heading for Istanbul. Another first in my life, I need Istanbul like the plague. With my fear of Turks.

MAGEE But you don't get to Istanbul.

MARION Halfway there we jump off the train.

WALTER I'm really looking forward to that. It's been so long since I've jumped off a moving train.

MAGEE Your contact will assist you in all these maneuvers.

MARION What are you so worried about?

WALTER We'll wait and see how well you jump. You practically break a leg finding a seat in the movies.

MARION After leaving the train, we're met by a man driving a wagonload of hay.

MAGEE Correct.

MARION We dress up as peasants, get up on the wagon and go with him.

WALTER It has to be hay, right. I got the worst hay fever in America. Must be hay.

MARION He takes us to the seashore where we're picked up by a submarine. Isn't it thrilling, Walter?

WALTER A submarine? Yesterday it was a plane.

MAGEE It had to be changed. Security precautions.

WALTER Thanks for telling me, I would have spent all day looking for wings.

MAGEE Now then, here's some local currency . . .

WALTER No, it's all right, I got money. You get the next one.

MARION Take it, Walter. You only have traveler's checks.

WALTER They're good anywhere.

MARION You're gonna stop in the middle of a chase through an alley and start signing traveler's checks?

WALTER What do you mean chasing through alleys? You said this was going to be simple. I can't run. I'm an old man with orthopedic shoes.

MAGEE (*Producing a revolver*) I suggest you take this money. Incidentally, have you ever shot a pistol?

WALTER Shot a pistol? How often in the catering business is there a gun fight?

MAGEE (*Handing it to* WALTER) It's very simple. It can't fire unless you release this safety catch. Then just squeeze the trigger.

WALTER (*Intrigued by it*) It's a beauty.

MARION I don't think you should carry a gun.

WALTER Why not?

MARION They're dangerous.

WALTER They're not dangerous.

MARION But you don't know how to use one.

WALTER Don't tell me, I can use a gun.

MARION When did you ever use a gun?

WALTER Plenty of times, don't worry . . .

MARION When?

WALTER I want to carry it.

MARION I don't want you to carry a gun.

WALTER Why can't I carry a gun? I want a gun. What's wrong? Why can't I have a gun?

MARION I'm not going if you carry a gun.

MAGEE Maybe Mrs. Hollander has a point. I'm being over-cautious. There won't be any need for it.

WALTER (*To* MARION) Why do you have to take the fun out of everything we do?

MARION All right, you can carry it, but keep it unloaded.

MAGEE You'd always have the time to load it. But you won't need it. I've got every angle figured.
(*He exits*)

WALTER (*A la Sam Spade*) You can never tell when this little piece of tin can spell the difference . . .

MARION (*Tensely*) Well—this is it.

WALTER Don't worry, it'll be a cinch.

MARION You got very confident all of a sudden.

WALTER Ah, everybody makes a big deal out of nothing.

MARION (*Getting teary*) You think so?

WALTER Sure, the whole thing'll be over in two hours. It won't be any worse an ordeal than your sister's wedding.

MARION (*Crying a bit now*) You think so?

WALTER What are you crying about? She's crying already.

MARION (*More crying*) I'm sorry.

WALTER Can't you go any place without crying? Every time we make plans you have to get upset. That's why I never want to go any place. And that's why I was not keen on escaping. Because I knew you'd make it into a federal case. What's the matter?

MARION I don't know.

93

WALTER What do you mean, you don't know? How can you not know what you're crying about? Does something hurt you?

MARION (*Crying*) I'm afraid . . .

WALTER Aha, you're not such a big shot any more. You talk a good game. Stop crying, everything's gonna be all right—come on—this is going to be simple as pie, there's nothing to be worried about. What's the worst thing that could happen? We'll get caught? Big deal. They'll try us and torture us? So what? We bite down on those cyanide capsules . . . (MARION *lets out a big wail*) Stop crying. Leave everything to me, will you please do that? Will you trust me . . . I know what I'm doing . . . I'll take care of us, don't worry. You think I'm gonna let anybody hurt you? You remember when we were first married, a soldier whistled at you at Palisades Amusement Park, I gave him a sock in the mouth.

MARION (*Reminiscing*) Yeah, he was a little tiny thing.

WALTER You were so beautiful in your puce Aztec shawl.

MARION And you with that dark-blue dress suit, with the white socks and the saddle shoes . . .

WALTER That was doctor's orders, I had a foot infection.

MARION Walter, will you protect me?

WALTER Have I ever let you down? Ever? Did I stand by you right from the start when my mother despised you?

94

Did I hold your hand through two pregnancies, four false alarms, and a very complicated oral prophylaxis? Now come on . . . Have a little faith in me. I'll see that we come out right side up.

MARION   Walter—I've been such a terrible wife . . .

WALTER   Not at all . . . I'm not easy to live with. You'd be amazed but a lot of women would find me unpleasant.

MARION   No.

WALTER   Sure. Now come on, go upstairs and rest for a while and then you ought to start getting ready.

MARION   I'm wearing my new dress.

WALTER   You better bring a pair of sneakers.

MARION   Wally.

WALTER   You haven't called me that since the Harvest Moon Ball and even then I said if you ever did, I'd break your neck . . .

MARION   I'm going, I'm going.
        (*She exits*)

WALTER   (*Calling after her*)   I'm gonna read my paper. I'll see you later. And don't worry—you're dealing with a guy who can handle himself.
        (*He removes the revolver, tries twirling it, and puts it in his belt. He walks across the stage like a constipated gun fighter ready to draw against his foe*)

KILROY (*Entering*) Mr. Hollander—
> (WALTER *turns rapidly, drawing his pistol, which goes off and nails* KILROY *in the leg.* KILROY *dances on one foot. Blackout*)

Lights come up on the party for the SULTAN. *The night is nearly over and only a few guests remain. The* SULTAN *and his* WIFE *are present, drinking heavily. The music is swinging, and fills the background.*

MAGEE (*Nervously looking to the stairway, awaiting the* HOLLANDERS' *entrance*) Ah, there you are, Your Majesty. Why don't you come inside and join the party? Did you enjoy being guest of honor?

SULTAN (*Quite tipsy*) Ah, Mr. Magee—there is nothing better to cement wounded pride than bourbon.

MAGEE (*He wants to get him out of the room*) Er, yes—there's plenty of bourbon inside.

SULTAN Whatever happened to the American from New Jersey. The mongrel.

MAGEE He couldn't come but he sends his apologies and best wishes. I'm delighted you consented to give us the opportunity to honor you, Your Majesty. You know how my father feels about you.

SULTAN Where is your father?

MAGEE He meant to get back for the party. But his plane was delayed. He'll probably come after everyone is gone. (SULTAN *and* WIFE *exit to the next room, unsteady.*

DROBNEY *enters suspiciously, cases the room, head-beckons* MAGEE *to come to him, which* MAGEE *does, sensing something's up)*

DROBNEY   Pick a card.

MAGEE   Now now, Father!

DROBNEY (*Forcing the deck on him*)   Go ahead—take one.

MAGEE   I'm not in the mood for magic.

DROBNEY   There's a message written on the two of spades.

MAGEE   You can tell me the message, Father. No one will hear.
(DROBNEY *tries to find the two of spades in a deck of obviously all two of spades. Finally he gets it*)

DROBNEY (*Reading the card*)   The Hollanders are ready.

MAGEE   That's the message?
(DROBNEY *goes off*)

SUSAN (*Coming down the stairs dressed as a guest at the reception*)   Axel.

MAGEE   Where are your parents?

SUSAN   They're coming. My father's having trouble getting his holster on.

MAGEE   The house is crawling with trouble. Krojack is here.

If I tried to keep anyone away it would look suspicious. You better move fast. The coast is clear.

SUSAN   Good-bye, Axel. I'll speak to you in a few days.

MAGEE   We have some future plans to discuss.
(*She exits toward the front hallway.* WALTER *and* MARION *come downstairs, and then suddenly reverse their tracks and run back up. We see why as the* SULTAN *crosses near the bottom of stairway. Now, with the* SULTAN *gone, they come down again and head straight for the front door. Suddenly we see them turn in horror and head back toward stairs to go up again.* KROJACK *is crossing toward them and he is the reason they turned, but now the path to the staircase is no good because the* SULTAN *is crossing back. The scene now is that* KROJACK *is walking toward the* SULTAN *with the* HOLLANDERS *in the middle. This all happens upstage and for a moment they are all hidden behind a center panel. After a second,* KROJACK *emerges, still heading in his direction and the* SULTAN *emerges, still heading in his. They cross and go offstage. Finally the* HOLLANDERS *emerge*)

MARION   Walter, you haven't hugged and kissed me like that in twenty-five years.

WALTER   That was you? What are we gonna do?

MARION   Try and appear casual.

WALTER   I am appearing casual.

MARION   You know, Walter, you can tell you're carrying a gun.

WALTER   Get out of here, you can not.

MARION   Walter, there's a big bulge under your shoulder.

WALTER   It's the way I'm built.

MARION   It's not the way you're built. You don't have a handle.

WALTER   Leave me alone.

MARION   Put it upstairs.

WALTER   We need it.

MARION   We don't need it. You shot Mr. Kilroy today; it's dangerous.

WALTER   It went off accidentally.

MARION   Walter, people are staring at your bulge.

WALTER   (*Hands on ears he crosses to get away from her and bumps into* KASNAR, *a guest*)   "A foggy day in London town . . ."

KASNAR   We have not met, have we?

WALTER   (*Lapsing into his speech*)   I'm John Randall from Washington, D.C. I work in the Department of the Interior, I'm married and I have four children. I was born in Milwaukee, Wisconsin, and went to school in California. I majored in agriculture and first entered Government under Roosevelt. I drive a Chrysler Imperial. I'm John Randall . . .

MARION (*Follows the story by rote, then joins in*) And I am his lovely wife, Carmen.

KASNAR How do you do? Yanis Kasnar, and this is the Countess Wilamena Bordoni.

COUNTESS Charmed.

MARION (*Pinching him*) Say hello to the Countess, darling.

WALTER (*Nervously*) Hello, darling.

KASNAR (*Holding up his glass*) This wine is extraordinary. Have you tasted it?

COUNTESS Uhmmm . . . Exquisite.
(WALTER *takes* KASNAR'S *glass, drains it in one gulp*)

KASNAR Yes, rather diffident and ephemeral, wouldn't you say, Mr. Randall?

WALTER (*Squirms a moment*) Hmm, the bouquet is subtly demure, yet the flavor is playfully articulate. (*Then aside to* MARION) *Esquire Magazine.*

KASNAR How long have you been here?
(*She and* WALTER *talk simultaneously*)

MARION Two weeks.

WALTER Just a few days.

MARION A few days.

WALTER Two weeks. We're at the big hotel . . .

MARION We're staying at the Grand Hotel.

WALTER I don't care for it.

MARION It's beautiful—well, we really must be going, it's late. Come, Walter.

KASNAR Walter?

WALTER (*With a nudge*) How amusing. My own wife forgets I'm Sam Randall.

KASNAR Sam?

MARION (*Correcting* WALTER) John.

WALTER John, Sam, Walter—my real name was Randall John Sam but everyone in Washington confused it with Lyndon Johnson—John Sam, Johnson—I kept getting all his meat bills and phone messages.

KASNAR How interesting.

WALTER (*To* MARION) Let's go. We're due in Afghanistan.

MARION Tunisia.

WALTER   Afghanistan, Tunisia . . . Come on, Marion.

COUNTESS   Marion?

MARION   I'm his lovely wife, Carmen.
        (*The* COUNTESS *drops her fan.* WALTER *goes to pick it up*)

WALTER   Allow me . . . OH! (*His pistol falls to the floor as he goes to pick up the fan. There is a tense moment. Everyone stares. He writhes. There is a pause*) My—my cigarette lighter.

KASNAR   (*An unlit cigarette in his mouth*)   May I have a light?
        (*Trapped,* WALTER *fakes trying to light the cigarette with his gun, and* MARION *stands back anticipating a shot. Finally nothing happens*)

WALTER   Damn Zippos, never work.

KASNAR   No matter. Well, we must be going. The party is about over and I hate to be the last to leave.
        (*He and the* COUNTESS *exit, leaving* WALTER *and* MARION *alone*)

MARION   Lucky those Zippos never work.

WALTER   C'mon, Marion.
        (*They start off when* KROJACK *enters*)

KROJACK   So, my friends, we meet again.

WALTER What'd you do, roll a drunk and steal his invitation?

KROJACK You're all dressed up. Are you going someplace?

DROBNEY (*Enters urgently*) Krojack—telephone call for you —urgent. Why don't you take it in my room, it's quiet up there. Hurry, they're holding.

KROJACK (*Wavers, then decides it might be important*) I will deal with you later.
  (*He goes off with* DROBNEY *and after he exits,* MARION *and* WALTER *head for the front door*)

MAGEE (*Entering with* BURNS) Where are they?

BURNS They've gone. Once they're past the police at the gate the rest is not hard.

MAGEE If we don't hear anything in the next two minutes we can assume they've made it.

BURNS (*Tensely imagining*) By now they're going down the front steps. Now they're going to the car—slowly—deliberately.

MAGEE Now they're up to the gate. They're going through all together. The police have no reason to stop them. (DROBNEY *runs down the stairs and crosses offstage.* KROJACK *follows after him in pursuit, only this time* KROJACK'S *wearing the strait jacket*) I wonder if this is happening in any other Embassy.
  (*Suddenly from outside we hear gunshots and commotion*)

BURNS What is it?

SUSAN (*Entering*) Oh, Axel—it's terrible.

MARION (*Entering, pale*) Walter, how could you do it?

WALTER (*Entering with smoking revolver in one hand*) It
    was dark—I couldn't see anything.
        (*Enter* AMBASSADOR MAGEE, *shot in the leg, and
        furious*)

MAGEE DAD!
                (*Blackout*)

SCENE 4

The lights come up. It is the next morning. AMBASSADOR
MAGEE *is in a wheelchair, furious with* AXEL.

AMBASSADOR   How could you do it? How could you attempt
an escape?

MAGEE   Dad, the situation called for something bold. If it
had worked, we'd all be heroes.

AMBASSADOR   But it failed, as everything you do fails.
Picketing, riots, bombs—this never happened in my Embassy before. And this morning a devout priest produced a
seven of spades from my ear.

MAGEE   Father Drobney was trying to cheer you up, sir.

AMBASSADOR   I'll get you for this, Axel, I'll find a way, I
promise.
    (SUSAN *enters*)

SUSAN   Excuse me.

AMBASSADOR   I'm finished with him, Miss Hollander. By the
way, your mother called. She wants you to mail her your
birth certificate. Through two world wars without a scratch
only to be shot by a caterer.
    (*And he wheels himself offstage*)

SUSAN   Axel, I'm sorry. It's all our fault.

MAGEE   No, it isn't. But now they've doubled the guard outside.

WALTER (*Entering with* MARION)   Well, Magee, it was a nice try. Unfortunately, I shot the boss, but those are the breaks.

MARION   I guess we're here for good now.

MAGEE   I got you into this and I promise I'll get you out.

WALTER   Well, I'm ready, willing and able to try anything. I feel I've been toughened up by our first attempt. Now that I've actually drawn blood. True, it was your father's . . .
     (*Moans from the other room are heard*)

MAGEE   What was that?

SUSAN (*Goes and peeks into the other room*)   It's the Sultan of Bashir and his wife, and are they unconscious.
     (MAGEE *goes to take a look*)

WALTER   Serves 'em right. They drank up enough alcohol last night to rub down the Green Bay Packers.

MARION   I better call Barney Silverman. He's probably still at Montauk Point with the station wagon waiting for us to surface.

MAGEE (*Returning with* BURNS)   Mr. Burns, the Sultan and his wife have had a little too much party. You better put them to bed. If you have trouble moving the Sultan, there's

a dolly downstairs. Find some pajamas for them—pajamas
—pajamas . . .
(*An idea has hit* MAGEE *and he sizes up* WALTER)

WALTER   Magee, why are you looking at me like that and
repeating the word pajamas?

MAGEE   I'll bet it would work.

SUSAN   Axel, what are you thinking?

MAGEE (*Yells*)   Father Drobney, come here quickly.

WALTER   Magee, if there's something going through that
mind of yours besides the usual cattle stampede you want
to tell us.

MAGEE (*Holds a pillow to* WALTER's *stomach*)   Size is about
right.

SUSAN   Axel, I know what you're thinking, but there's two
of them and three of us.

MAGEE   No one saw them leave last night, so if they leave
now it'll look perfectly natural. Except underneath those
royal robes will not be His Majesty at all but the phantom
caterer!

WALTER   It sounds great! It won't work, but it sounds great!

MARION   It's just crazy enough to work.

MAGEE   You two change quickly.

108

(He hustles WALTER *and* MARION *into the room with the unconscious* SULTAN*)*

SUSAN What about me?

MAGEE I'll come to you. Mr. Burns, please assist them.
(He closes the door on all of them)

SUSAN Axel, are you sure you know what you're doing?

MAGEE Susan, for the first time since this whole thing started I feel in complete control. This is going to work.
(Enter DROBNEY*)*

DROBNEY You called?

MAGEE Yes, Father. Are your contacts still ready to go on a moment's notice?

DROBNEY Yes, I'm sure.

MAGEE Then alert them quickly.
*(*DROBNEY *quickly gets on the phone)*

SUSAN Axel. This is so thrilling. You're actually having an idea.

MAGEE Susan. Every now and then fate comes along, takes a man by the hand and enables him to build a mountain.

SUSAN *(Thrilled)* Oh, Axel! How corny!

MAGEE Susan. I'm going to get you all home safely—right now.

DROBNEY (*Into the phone, significantly*) The storm we were expecting will be a little late. I think the same precautions are in order.

MAGEE Susan. Have I told you lately that I love you?

SUSAN No. But if you want to I think we can work something out.

DROBNEY Ready to go?
(WALTER *and* MARION *come onstage, dressed as the* SULTAN *and his* WIFE)

WALTER His suit itches.

MARION How can it itch? It's silk.

WALTER I've explained a thousand times about my skin. My dermatologist says I've got the thighs of a princess.

DROBNEY (*Hanging up the phone*) Everything is ready. Go immediately. God bless you.

MAGEE Try to be as casual and confident as you can and if anyone talks to you, mutter something about Allah.

DROBNEY The driver will take you to the Grand Hotel. From there on our plan will be precisely the same.

MARION What about Susan?

MAGEE She's going to walk out with me in a little while under the protection of full diplomatic immunity.

SUSAN   How?

MAGEE   As the wife of a foreign diplomat, you get that privilege.

WALTER   Wife? You and her?

MAGEE   Why not? We're United States citizens in United States territory. We're over twenty-one and Father Drobney is a priest. It's perfect.

SUSAN   (*Thrilled*)   Oh, Axel.

MARION   (*Hugging* SUSAN)   My Susan a bride. This is the happiest day of my life. I only wish your father were alive to see it.

WALTER   I am alive. I'm right here.

MARION   Oh, I'm sorry, dear—I got carried away.

SUSAN   Axel, it's brilliant!

WALTER   What if she doesn't want to marry you?

SUSAN   I do, I do.

WALTER   You do? (*To* MAGEE)   May Allah twist your nose off.

MAGEE   We've got to act fast.

MARION   (*To* SUSAN)   While we're aboard the submarine, you wire us your silverware pattern.

WALTER (*To* MAGEE) May all the sands of the desert fill your navel.

SUSAN See you in Newark in a few days.

MAGEE Hurry—please.

WALTER Come on, Marion—I better get home and register his name at the unemployment insurance office.

MARION (*To* SUSAN) On the way home I'll stop at the drugstore and send you a bottle of those pills.

MAGEE (*Proudly*) Mr. Hollander. Remember, sir, you're not losing a daughter—you're gaining a son.

WALTER May all the camels in Egypt . . . Ah, forget it.
    (*He and* MARION *exit*)

DROBNEY (*Stepping forward and addressing the audience as* MAGEE *and* SUSAN *kiss and freeze*) Incidentally, the Hollanders made it safely to Newark. I married Susan and Magee. And Ambassador Magee is still running for governor without the Sultan's help. And just to be sure no one causes any trouble he sent Magee five thousand miles away to Bolivia, where for the first time in two hundred years that country had a plague of *locusts*. (*To* MAGEE *and* SUSAN) Pick a card—go ahead—pick a card.
    (*Music up*)
                    (*Curtain*)